SERIES EDITOR: ALAN SMITH

# Modular Maths
## for Edexcel

# Decision Mathematics 1

## Second Edition

- ◆ **ALAN SMITH**
- ◆ **KEITH PARRAMORE, JOAN STEPHENS, CHRIS COMPTON, GEOFF RIGBY**

Hodder Murray
A MEMBER OF THE HODDER HEADLINE GROUP

The Publishers would like to thank the following for permission to reproduce copyright material:

## Acknowledgements

OCR, AQA and London Qualifications Ltd accept no responsibility whatsoever for the accuracy or method of working in the answers given.

All questions acknowledged as MEI are reproduced with the kind permission of OCR/MEI.

All questions acknowledged as Edexcel are reproduced with the kind permission of London Qualifications Ltd, trading as Edexcel Limited.

AQA (AEB) examination questions are reproduced by the permission of the Assessment and Qualifications Alliance. Please note that the following AQA (AEB) question used (p.122) is NOT from the live examinations for the current specification. For GCE Advanced Level subjects, new specifications were introduced in 2001.

For questions acknowledged as belonging to 'Oxford' copyright is held by OCR (Oxford Cambridge and RSA Examinations). Please note that the Oxford questions used are not from the live examinations for the current specification.

p.22 London Underground diagram reproduced with kind permission of Transport for London; p.23 Geographically-nearly-accurate tube map reproduced with kind permission of Simon Clarke.

Every effort has been made to trace all copyright holders, but if any have been inadvertently overlooked the Publishers will be pleased to make the necessary arrangements at the first opportunity.

Hodder Headline's policy is to use papers that are natural, renewable and recyclable products and made from wood grown in sustainable forests. The logging and manufacturing processes are expected to conform to the environmntal regulations of the country of origin.

Orders: please contact Bookpoint Ltd, 130 Milton Park, Abingdon, Oxon OX14 4SB. Telephone: (44) 01235 827720. Fax: (44) 01235 400454. Lines are open 9.00–6.00, Monday to Saturday, with a 24-hour message answering service. Visit our website at www.hoddereducation.co.uk

© Alan Smith 2005
First published in 2005 by
Hodder Murray, an imprint of Hodder Education,
a member of the Hodder Headline Group
338 Euston Road
London NW1 3BH

Impression number   10  9  8  7  6  5  4  3  2  1
Year                        2010  2009  2008  2007  2006  2005

Cover photo from The Image Bank/Getty Images.
Illustrations: pp.22, 23 redrawn by Barking Dog Art; p.64 Königsberg by Cartoon Studio.
Typeset in 10pt Sabon by Pantek Arts Ltd, Maidstone, Kent.
Printed by Martins the Printers Ltd, Berwick Upon Tweed.

A catalogue record for this title is available from the British Library

ISBN-10: 0340 90732 0
ISBN-13: 978 0 340 907 320

# EDEXCEL ADVANCED MATHEMATICS

The Edexcel course is based on units in the four strands of Pure Mathematics, Mechanics, Statistics and Decision Mathematics. The first unit in each of these strands is designated AS, and so is Pure Mathematics: Core 2; all the others are A2.

The units may be aggregated as follows:

| | |
|---|---|
| 3 units | AS Mathematics |
| 6 units | A Level Mathematics |
| 9 units | A Level Mathematics + AS Further Mathematics |
| 12 units | A Level Mathematics + A Level Further Mathematics |

Core 1 and 2 are compulsory for AS Mathematics, and Core 3 and 4 must also be included in a full A Level award.

Examinations are offered by Edexcel twice a year, in January (most units) and in June (all units). All units are assessed by examination only; there is no longer any coursework in the scheme.

Candidates are not permitted to use electronic calculators in the Core 1 examination. In all other examinations candidates may use any legal calculator of their choice, including graphical calculators.

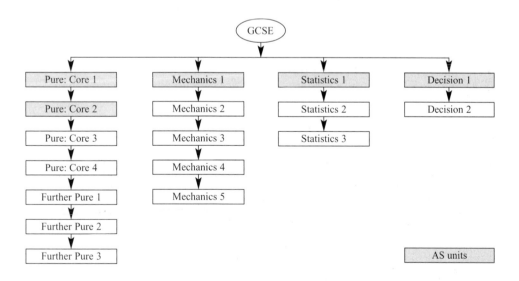

# INTRODUCTION

This book is one of a series written for the Edexcel Advanced Mathematics scheme. It has been adapted from the successful series written for the MEI Structured Mathematics scheme, and has been substantially edited and rewritten to provide complete coverage of the new Edexcel Decision Mathematics unit.

There are seven chapters in the book. These are presented in syllabus order, and begin by covering Algorithms and then Networks, followed by a short chapter on Route Inspection. Chapters 4 and 5 cover Critical Path Analysis and Linear Programming. Finally the book returns to graph theory, finishing with two chapters on Matchings and Flows in Networks. Each chapter contains a number of past examination questions.

You may wish to study the material in a different order, so the chapters are designed to stand alone if required, though you may occasionally need to refer to definitions earlier in the book.

Do remember that many of the methods used to solve Decision Mathematics problems are dynamic processes, and may initially appear difficult when presented in printed form. With perseverance you should discover that such methods are simpler than they seem at first sight!

I would like to thank the many people who have helped in the preparation and checking of material. Special thanks are due to Keith Parramore, Joan Stephens, Chris Compton and Geoff Rigby, who wrote the original MEI material. Finally, I am most grateful to Susie Jameson, who previewed the manuscript and suggested a number of improvements, and to Penny Nicholson, whose careful editing has helped to lighten some of the more difficult topics.

Alan Smith

# CONTENTS

# ALGORITHMS

Houston, we've had a problem here.

*Jack Swigert (Astronaut,* Apollo 13*)*

● ● ● ● ● ● ● ● ● ● ● ● ● ● ● ●

## INTRODUCING ALGORITHMS

An *algorithm* is simply a set of instructions which are followed in sequence to achieve a solution to a mathematical problem.

When you have multiplied two decimals together, for example, you have used an algorithm to achieve this. Solving quadratic equations by the formula is another example of an algorithm at work.

Many of the topics in decision mathematics are based on the idea of an algorithm. In this first chapter you will be introduced to some general ideas about algorithms, as well as learning some particular ones that can help to solve packing, sorting and searching problems.

Do you happen to know on which day of the week you were born? If not, here is an algorithm that can help you find out.

**Zeller's algorithm**

Let day number = D
month number  = M
and year         = Y.

If M is 1 or 2 add 12 to M and subtract 1 from Y.

Let C be the first two digits of Y and Y′ be the last two digits of Y.

Add together the integer parts of (2.6M – 5.39), (Y′/4) and (C/4), then add on D and Y′ and subtract 2C. (Integer part of 2.3 is 2, of 6.7 is 6, i.e. the whole number part, but note that integer part of –1.7 is –2 and 3.1 is –4, etc.)

**Example: 15 May 1991**

D = 15
M = 5
Y = 1991




C = 19
Y′ = 91

7 + 22 + 4 + 15 + 91 – 38 = 101

Find the remainder when this quantity is divided by 7.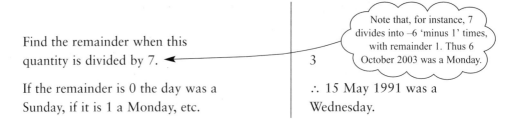

3

Note that, for instance, 7 divides into –6 'minus 1' times, with remainder 1. Thus 6 October 2003 was a Monday.

If the remainder is 0 the day was a Sunday, if it is 1 a Monday, etc.

∴ 15 May 1991 was a Wednesday.

Try Zeller's algorithm to discover the day of the week on which you were born.

## FLOWCHARTS

Many algorithms involve some element of repetition, so they can be written in a compact form using a *flowchart*. This is simply a diagram in which instructions and questions are written inside boxes with a set of arrows linking them together. By following the arrows you are carrying out the steps of the algorithm.

Look at the flowchart in figure 1.1. Can you see what it is designed to achieve?

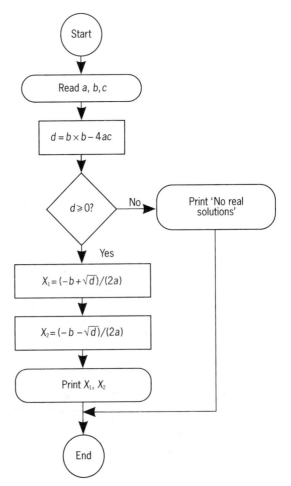

Start

Read $a, b, c$

$d = b \times b - 4ac$

$d \geqslant 0$?    No→    Print 'No real solutions'

Yes

$X_1 = (-b + \sqrt{d})/(2a)$

$X_2 = (-b - \sqrt{d})/(2a)$

Print $X_1, X_2$

End

FIGURE 1.1

Hopefully, you will have recognised that this flowchart finds the solutions to a quadratic equation of the form $ax^2 + bx + c = 0$.

Notice that instructions are placed in rectangular or oval boxes, whereas simple Yes/No questions go inside diamond-shaped boxes.

Here is another flowchart. Can you see what this one does?

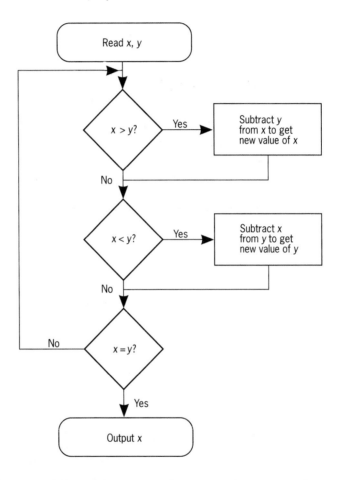

FIGURE 1.2

Notice that the general flow is from top to bottom, unless you are following back up in response to a question.

One way to understand the flowchart is to try it out with some numbers, say $x = 24$ and $y = 32$. The 'Is $x = y$?' box will return an answer of 'No' several times, so the process repeats several times, with changing values of $x$ and $y$. You can draw a table to keep track of how these are changing.

| | $x$ | $y$ |
|---|---|---|
| Input | 24 | 32 |
| | 24 | 8 |
| | 16 | 8 |
| | 8 | 8 |
| Output | 8 | |

The flowchart is actually finding the highest common factor, or HCF, of 24 and 32, by repeated subtraction. The underlying method is called Euclid's algorithm.

**Historical note**    Euclid of Alexandria, who lived from about 325 to 265 BC, is now best remembered for his monumental work on geometry, *The Elements*. He also worked extensively in other fields, including algebra and number theory. In Book IX of *The Elements*, Euclid gave an elegant proof that there are infinitely many prime numbers.

The algorithms discussed so far, namely Zeller's, Euclid's and the quadratic formula, are not explicitly stated on your examination specification, so you would not be expected to learn them by heart; if an examination question wanted you to use any of these, then you would be given the necessary instructions, probably in the form of a flowchart. The short exercise below gives you a chance to practise interpreting flowcharts, before you move on to the packing, sorting and searching algorithms that you are expected to learn.

EXERCISE 1A

1  The physicist Albert Einstein was born in Ulm, Bavaria, on 14th March 1879. Use Zeller's algorithm (page 1) to determine on what day of the week he was born.

2  Use the flowchart for Euclid's algorithm (figure 1.2) to find the highest common factor of
(a)  70 and 98                          (b)  144 and 360.

Write down all the intermediate values in your calculation.

3  (a)  Run the flowchart below starting with the numbers A = 2, B = 3, C = 4 and D = 7, to find the values of the outputs X and Y.

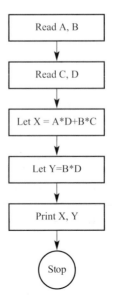

**(b)** In fact the numbers A, B, C, D represent the fractions $\frac{A}{B}$ and $\frac{C}{D}$. Explain what the algorithm is achieving.

**(c)** Oliver says 'If you apply this algorithm in this way to the fractions $\frac{1}{2}$ and $\frac{1}{4}$ you will get an answer of $\frac{3}{4}$.' Is he right?

**4** The following steps define an algorithm which operates on two numbers.

Step 1   Write down the two numbers side by side on the same line.

Step 2   Beneath the left-hand number write down double that number. Beneath the right-hand number write down half of that number, ignoring any remainder.

Step 3   Repeat step 2 until the right-hand number is 1.

Step 4   Delete those rows where the number in the right-hand column is even. Add up the remaining numbers in the left-hand column. This is the result.

**(a)** Apply the algorithm to the numbers 50 and 56.

**(b)** Use your result from part **(a)**, and any other simpler examples you may choose, to write down what the algorithm achieves.

[MEI]

# BIN PACKING

An important problem in decision mathematics is 'bin packing'. This is the ability to fill containers with varying sized objects in an efficient way. Problems to do with cutting also belong under this heading. There is, as yet, no known algorithm that will always give the optimal solution, but there are three algorithms in common use that you need to know.

**EXAMPLE 1.1**

Mary wants to record some programmes on to videotape. Each tape is 3 hours long. The lengths of the programmes are as follows.

$\frac{1}{2}$ hour,     2 hours,     1 hour,     $\frac{3}{4}$ hour,     $1\frac{1}{2}$ hours,     2 hours,     $\frac{3}{4}$ hour

Produce a suitable plan to use the videotapes efficiently.

*Solution*   Obviously, one solution would be to record each programme on to a fresh tape! This is a rather extravagant solution since seven tapes would be required with a lot of wastage on each. There are three different approaches you can use to find a more efficient solution.

**Method 1: The first fit algorithm**

Take each programme in turn, and record it on to the first tape on which it will fit, i.e. try tape 1 and, if it doesn't fit, then try tape 2, and so on.

The $\frac{1}{2}$ hour and 2 hour programmes will both fit on to tape number 1.

FIGURE 1.3

Next, there is a 1 hour programme. This will not fit on to the first tape, so you have to use tape number 2.

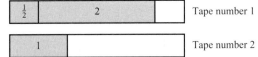

FIGURE 1.4

Continuing in a similar way, you arrive at this solution.

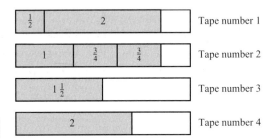

FIGURE 1.5

Notice that this solution still has quite a lot of wastage, although the requirement is reduced to just four tapes.

**Method 2: The first fit decreasing algorithm**

This is identical to method 1, apart from just one step: you arrange the items in decreasing order of size first, then apply the first fit algorithm to the new list.

So, the list becomes as follows.

$$2 \quad 2 \quad 1\frac{1}{2} \quad 1 \quad \frac{3}{4} \quad \frac{3}{4} \quad \frac{1}{2}$$

Then, applying first fit to this new list, you obtain this solution.

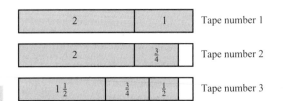

FIGURE 1.6

Clearly this is a better solution. It requires only three tapes, and there is only $\frac{1}{2}$ hour of wasted tape, shared between tapes 2 and 3.

**Method 3: The full bin algorithm**

Strictly speaking, this is not really an algorithm at all. You simply try to spot combinations that make up a full bin, or full tape in this context.

Obviously, $2 + 1$ gives a full 3 hour tape; so does $1\frac{1}{2} + \frac{3}{4} + \frac{3}{4}$. So you have this solution.

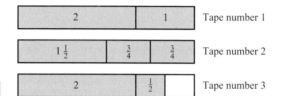

FIGURE 1.7

Again you have three tapes with $\frac{1}{2}$ hour of waste, but notice that this time the waste is all on a single tape so, if Mary wanted to record another $\frac{1}{2}$ hour programme, it could be done. This is clearly the best solution of all: in fact it is *optimal* (the best possible solution) in terms of wasted tape.

To be absolutely sure that you have found the best solution, you ought to check every possible feasible combination of programmes, but that would take far too long to be of much use. In general, you can summarise the behaviour of these three methods as follows.

**First fit**              Quick and simple, but rarely finds an optimal solution.

**First fit decreasing**   Only slightly longer than first fit and often succeeds in finding a solution that is close to optimal.

**Full bin algorithm**    Can produce very efficient solutions but difficult to use in practice as it relies on operator skill to spot suitable groupings. An automated version would require checking far too many combinations to be practical.

As a general rule of thumb, the first fit decreasing algorithm usually offers a good compromise between efficiency and ease of use.

EXERCISE 1B

1  Six items with the weights given in the table are to be packed into boxes, each of which has a capacity of 10 kg.

| Item | A | B | C | D | E | F |
|------|---|---|---|---|---|---|
| Weight (kg) | 2 | 1 | 6 | 3 | 3 | 5 |

(a) Use the first fit algorithm to pack the boxes, saying how many boxes are needed.

(b) Give an optimal solution.

[MEI]

**2** The following eight lengths of pipe are to be cut from three pieces, each of length 2 metres.

$$1.1, \quad 1.2, \quad 0.3, \quad 0.4, \quad 0.2, \quad 0.4, \quad 0.3, \quad 0.7 \text{ metres}$$

(a) Use the first fit decreasing algorithm to find a plan for cutting the lengths of pipe.

(b) Suppose it is preferable to be left with a small number of longer pieces of pipe, rather than a larger number of shorter lengths. Use any method to produce an improved cutting plan.

[MEI]

**3** A carpenter wants to cut nine pieces of timber from planks. The lengths, in centimetres, are as follows.

$$45 \quad 60 \quad 35 \quad 20 \quad 40 \quad 30 \quad 50 \quad 55 \quad 25$$

He has a stock of planks each of length 120 centimetres.

(a) Use the first fit algorithm to find out how many planks are needed, and which pieces are cut from the same planks.

(b) Solve the problem again using the first fit decreasing algorithm.

(c) Solve the problem again using the full bin algorithm.

(d) Explain briefly which of your three solutions is the most efficient, giving a supporting reason.

In the previous section the simple first fit bin packing algorithm was adapted by sorting the items into order of size first. This is not always so easy as it sounds, especially when you have a large number of items to sort. This section looks in detail at two different methods for achieving this goal: bubble sort and quick sort.

# BUBBLE SORT

Here is a list of ten students in an A level class. They are in no particular order.

TOM
DUNCAN
ADELE
ATO
JADE
BETH
KASRA
JOE
TIM
AL

Although you can easily sort them into alphabetical order yourself, this does depend on the facts that you have learned the alphabet and can spot the right order by eye. A computer would need to check whether the items are in the right order by making comparisons, and exchanging any that are in the wrong place. Bubble sort is a standard method of doing this.

To carry out a bubble sort, you start at the top of the list. Compare the first two items. If they are the wrong way round, then exchange them, otherwise leave them as they are. Then compare the second and third items, exchanging them if they are in the wrong order. Continue in this way until you have compared the last two items.

Try this procedure out on the list above. You should get the list below.

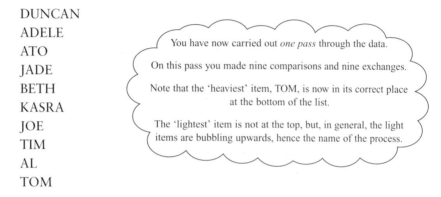

DUNCAN
ADELE
ATO
JADE
BETH
KASRA
JOE
TIM
AL
TOM

You have now carried out *one pass* through the data.

On this pass you made nine comparisons and nine exchanges.

Note that the 'heaviest' item, TOM, is now in its correct place at the bottom of the list.

The 'lightest' item is not at the top, but, in general, the light items are bubbling upwards, hence the name of the process.

Of course, you can guarantee that the heaviest item will have made its way to the bottom of the list after one pass. So you now repeat the whole process, but stopping when you have compared the second-to-last pair.

The result of the second pass will look like this.

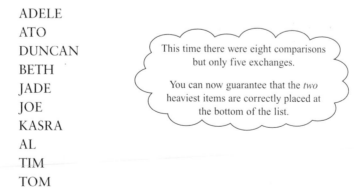

ADELE
ATO
DUNCAN
BETH
JADE
JOE
KASRA
AL
TIM
TOM

This time there were eight comparisons but only five exchanges.

You can now guarantee that the *two* heaviest items are correctly placed at the bottom of the list.

To complete the bubble sort, you simply continue to make further passes through the data, progressively stopping one place higher up the list each time. You stop when no exchanges have been made on a particular pass, since this indicates that the list is now in the right order.

Here is the final sorted list.

ADELE
AL
ATO
BETH
DUNCAN
JADE
JOE
KASRA
TIM
TOM

The amount of work required to sort a list using bubble sort will depend on how jumbled the data were to begin with. If they were in perfect reverse order, then you will need to make $\frac{n(n-1)}{2}$ comparisons and $\frac{n(n-1)}{2}$ exchanges. In the example above you might have needed as many as $\frac{10 \times 9}{2} = 45$ exchanges, although in fact you only needed 21 because the list was partially in order to begin with.

For a long list the bubble sort can become quite unmanageable, so an alternative algorithm such as quick sort might be used instead.

## QUICK SORT

The quick sort algorithm depends upon breaking the list up into smaller sublists, which rapidly reduces the intricacy of the sorting procedure. Here is how it works.

Step 1     Label the middle item in the list, by ringing it. This item forms the *pivot*.

Step 2     Take each item in turn, starting with the first, and compare it with the pivot. Write those items which are lower in value to the left of the pivot and those which are higher, to the right. *Do not sort the items in any other way.*

Step 3     Continue to apply steps 1 and 2 to all sub-lists of length 2 or more.

**Note**          For an even number of items there will be a middle pair. Here the item in the later position of the two is selected as the pivot.

**EXAMPLE 1.2**

Use quick sort to arrange this list of numbers in increasing order of size. Show the results at the end of each pass.

10    7    22    25    18    19    11    6

*Solution*

The middle pair is 25 and 18; ring the later one, 18.

Write each item on the left or right depending on whether it is lower or higher than the pivot, 18.

At the end of pass 1 the list looks like this.

10    7    11    6    (18)    22    25    19

Ring 11 in the first sublist and 25 in the second.

Compare the items in each sublist with their respective pivot values, 11 or 25.

At the end of pass 2 the list looks like this.

10    7    6    (11)    (18)    22    19    (25)

For pass 3 the pivot value for the first sublist is 7 and for the second is 19.

At the end of pass 3 the list looks like this.

6    (7)    10    (11)    (18)    (19)    22    (25)

So the final sorted list is as follows.

6    7    10    11    18    19    22    25

**Historical note**

The quick sort algorithm was developed by the British computer scientist Sir Tony Hoare in 1960. It is arguably the world's most widely used algorithm of any kind.

EXERCISE 1C

**1 (a)** Use the bubble sort algorithm to arrange these numbers in increasing order of size. Show the results of each pass as you work through the algorithm.

10    35    8    66    39    17    44    52

**(b)** Repeat, using quick sort.

**2** Nine contestants take part in a cookery contest. Their scores, together with their surnames in alphabetical order, are given in the table.

| | |
|---|---|
| Andrews | 35 |
| Costa | 44 |
| Davis | 22 |
| Greene | 27 |
| Ha | 35 |
| Khataria | 38 |
| Miller | 21 |
| Oliver | 56 |
| Smith | 45 |

Use bubble sort to arrange the contestants in increasing order of their scores.

**3** An algorithm is being used to sort a set of numbers into ascending order of size. This is the unsorted list.

16   9   4   6   12   3   8   7

Here is the algorithm.

Step 1    Make a list of the $n$ numbers in the given order.

Step 2    On the $r$th pass, compare the first number with the second, then the second with the third, and so on, until $n - r$ comparisons have been made. At each comparison, the two numbers should be switched if they are in the wrong order.

Step 3    Repeat step 2 until $n - 1$ passes have been completed.

(a) Show the result of applying this algorithm, giving the result of each pass in your working.

(b) What name is given to this algorithm?

**4** An algorithm for sorting a list of different numbers into ascending order is described below.

Step 1    Write down the middle number in the list and circle it to show that it is not to be examined again.

Step 2    Compare the first number in the list with the circled number and write it before the circled number if it is less, or after if it is greater.

Step 3     Compare the next number in the list with the circled number and write it before or after, as in step 2. Write it after any other number that has already been dealt with in this part of the algorithm. (Note that this means that only one comparison is made – with the circled number.)

Step 4     Continue until the last element in the list has been dealt with. Note that the process will have created two sub-lists, one before the circled number and one after, either of which could be empty.

Step 5     Continue to apply the process to sub-lists of length two or more.

(a) Use this algorithm to sort the list {13, 56, 2, 40, 10, 50, 35}. Show all of your steps and count the number of comparisons that you have to make.

(b) Find the number of comparisons required to sort the list {7, 6, 5, 4, 3, 2, 1} into ascending order using this algorithm.

(c) What name is given to this algorithm?

[MEI, *part*]

# BINARY SEARCH

Imagine you are a receptionist at a dental practice. You have a drawer containing 99 patient files, all in alphabetical order, but with no names on the outsides of the files to distinguish them. Thus you have to look inside a file to see which patient it refers to.

The dentist asks you to find Mr Jones' file.

What method might you use?

There are several approaches to this problem, which is concerned with finding an efficient *search* procedure. A simple method is that of *binary search*. This is how it works.

First, select the middle file, in this case the 50th. Open it and look inside. Suppose it says 'Mr Edrich'. You may now discard (i.e. ignore) the first 50 files and you know the one you are looking for is in the second half, so there are now only 49 files to consider.

The next step is to divide the 49 remaining files at the middle position too, i.e. the 25th of these. If this time the name is 'Ms Patel' then you know that Mr Jones is in the first 24 files, and you discard the other 25.

Continue in a similar way, halving the number of items to be searched each time, until the search is successful.

This method is called binary search because of its close relationship with the binary number system, which is based on 1, 2, 4, 8, 16 and so on. If you are searching in a pile of 15 items, the first try will reduce this to 7, then 3, then 1, then success, so (at most) four tries are needed. Note that 15 is $2^4 - 1$. In general, binary search will guarantee to have found the item you are searching for after $n$ tries, provided the total number of items to be searched does not exceed $2^n - 1$. (Of course, this assumes the file does actually exist. In reality, it might be that Mr Jones does not yet have a file.)

### EXAMPLE 1.3

(a) Perform a binary search to find the name PATEL in the list AHMED, AUSTIN, EDRICH, FOSTER, GRACE, JONES, PATEL, SOMERS, WRIGHT.

(b) How many tries would be necessary in order to guarantee finding an item if you were using binary search in a list of 100 items?

*Solution*

(a) The list consists of nine items. The middle item is the fifth name.

AHMED, AUSTIN, EDRICH, FOSTER, GRACE, JONES, PATEL, SOMERS, WRIGHT

The fifth name is GRACE; this is too low, so you reject it and the first half of the list.

JONES, PATEL, SOMERS, WRIGHT

There are two middle items, the second and third names; pick the later one, i.e. the third. SOMERS is too high, so you reject it and the item(s) after it.

JONES, PATEL

Pick the later of the two remaining names, i.e. the second. This is PATEL so it has taken three tries to find the target item.

(b) For 100 items,

$2^6 - 1 = 63,$      so six tries is not enough.

$2^7 - 1 = 127,$      so seven tries is sufficient.

You can guarantee success within at most seven tries.

Notice that if the list contains an odd number of items, then it is easy to identify the middle one. If there is an even number of items, you usually pick the later one of the pair in the middle position.

**EXERCISE 1D**

**1** Show how a binary search is used to locate the name LARA in this list.

> JENNY, KELLY, LARA, MARTHA, NAOMI, OPAL, PANDORA

Write down each step of the binary search procedure.

**2** Show how a binary search is used to locate the name GARETH in this list.

> ALAN, BEN, CARLO, DEVON, EUGENE, FERGUS, GARETH, HAL, IAN

Write down each step of the binary search procedure.

**3** In a two-person game, one player thinks of a word and invites the other to guess what that word is. In response to an incorrect guess the first player indicates whether the mystery word is before or after the guess in alphabetical (dictionary) order.

**(a)** Given that a dictionary is available, describe a strategy for the second player to follow in trying to find the word in as few guesses as possible.

**(b)** Given that the dictionary has approximately 100 000 words, find the maximum number of guesses which might be required to find the mystery word using your method from part **(a)**.
Explain your reasoning in arriving at this number.

[MEI, *part*]

**EXERCISE 1E EXAMINATION-STYLE QUESTIONS**

**1 (a)** Use the binary search algorithm to locate the name HUSSAIN in the following alphabetical list. Explain each step of the algorithm.

1. ALLEN
2. BALL
3. COOPER
4. EVANS
5. HUSSAIN
6. JONES
7. MICHAEL
8. PATEL
9. RICHARDS
10. TINDALL
11. WU

**(b)** State the maximum number of comparisons that need to be made to locate a name in an alphabetical list of 11 names.

[Edexcel]

2 (a) Use the bubble sort algorithm to sort the list of numbers below into descending order showing the rearranged order after each pass.

90, 50, 55, 40, 20, 35, 30, 25, 45

Jessica wants to record a number of television programmes on to video tapes. Each tape is 2 hours long. The lengths, in minutes, of the programmes she wishes to record are:

55, 45, 20, 30, 30, 40, 20, 90, 25, 50, 35 and 35.

(b) Find the total length of programmes to be recorded and hence determine a lower bound for the number of tapes required.

(c) Use the first fit decreasing algorithm to fit the programmes on to her 2-hour tapes.

Jessica's friend Amy says she can fit all the programmes on to four tapes.

(d) Show how this is possible.

[Edexcel]

3 (a) Use the binary search algorithm to try to locate the name SABINE in the following alphabetical list. Explain each step of the algorithm.

    1. ABLE
    2. BROWN
    3. COOKE
    4. DANIEL
    5. DOUBLE
    6. FEW
    7. OSBORNE
    8. PAUL
    9. SWIFT
  10. TURNER

(b) Find the maximum number of iterations of the binary search algorithm needed to locate a name in a list of 1000 names.

[Edexcel]

**4** The table shows the points obtained by each of the teams in a football league after they had each played six games.
The teams are listed in alphabetical order. Carry out a quick sort to produce a list of teams in descending order of points obtained.

| Ashford | 6 |
|---|---|
| Colnbrook | 1 |
| Datchet | 18 |
| Feltham | 12 |
| Halliford | 9 |
| Laleham | 0 |
| Poyle | 5 |
| Staines | 13 |
| Wraysbury | 14 |

[Edexcel]

**5** An algorithm is described by the flowchart below.

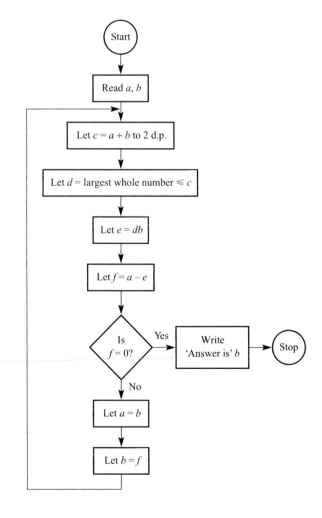

(a) Given that $a = 645$ and $b = 255$, make a table to show the results obtained at each step when the algorithm is applied.

(b) Explain how your solution to part (a) would be different if you had been given that $a = 255$ and $b = 645$.

(c) State what the algorithm achieves.

[Edexcel]

6 (a) The list of numbers below is to be sorted into descending order. Perform a bubble sort to obtain the sorted list, giving the state of the list after each complete pass.

$$55 \quad 80 \quad 25 \quad 84 \quad 25 \quad 34 \quad 17 \quad 75 \quad 3 \quad 5$$

The numbers in the list represent weights, in grams, of objects which are to be packed into bins that hold up to 100 g.

(b) Determine the least number of bins needed.

(c) Use the first fit decreasing algorithm to fit the objects into bins which hold up to 100 g.

[Edexcel]

7 Eleven boxes are to be packed into crates each of which has a weight limit of 100 kg. There are three boxes of weight 50 kg, three of weight 40 kg, three of weight 30 kg and two of weight 20 kg.

(a) Apply the first fit decreasing algorithm and state the number of crates used.

(b) Show that there is a solution using fewer crates.

[MEI]

8 The managing director of a chain of fast food restaurants wishes to have a ranked list showing the performances of his restaurant managers. Each manager is to be allocated a score, which is a whole number between 0 and 100, depending on the profitability and efficiency of the restaurant. The surnames of the managers are then to be sorted by their scores, those with the highest scores being at the top of the list.

(a) Five managers, together with their scores, are listed below. Use a bubble sort to put these managers into the required order, showing the list at the end of each pass. Give the number of comparisons made by the sort.

Cavill, 63;   Pippard, 81;   Dixon, 24;   Watson, 52;   Conway, 79

(b) What would a bubble sort do with two managers who have the same score?

(c) Put the managers into the required order using quick sort.

[MEI, *adapted*]

9 Thirteen books are to be stacked on shelves, each of which is of width 20 cm. The thicknesses of the books (in centimetres) are as follows.

$$4 \quad 1 \quad 5.5 \quad 2 \quad 6 \quad 1.5 \quad 1.5 \quad 2 \quad 2 \quad 4 \quad 5 \quad 3 \quad 2.5$$

(a) Arrange the books in increasing order of size. Taking the thinnest first, stack each book on the first shelf on which it will go. Show which size books go on which shelves using this method.

(b) Arrange the books in order of size and use the first fit decreasing algorithm to stack them on shelves. Show which size books go on which shelves using this method.

(c) Use the first fit algorithm on the original unsorted list to show that the books can be stacked on just two shelves.

[MEI]

10 The following flowchart defines an algorithm which operates on two inputs, $x$ and $y$.

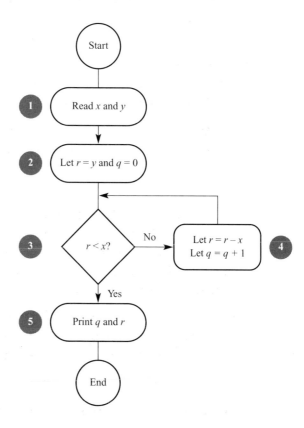

(a) Run the algorithm with inputs of $x = 3$ and $y = 41$, counting how many times the instructions in box number 4 are repeated.

(b) Say what the algorithm achieves.

The following flowchart defines an algorithm that operates on three inputs, $x$, $y_1$ and $y_2$.

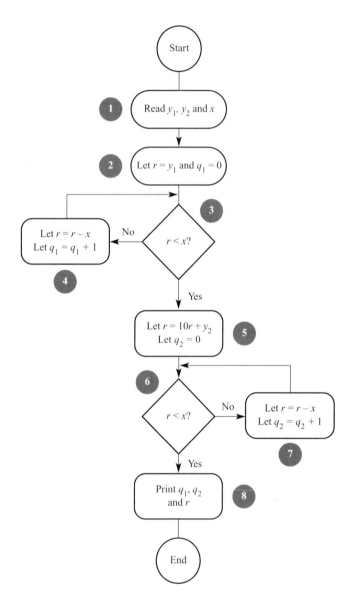

(c) Work through the algorithm with $x = 3$, $y_1 = 4$ and $y_2 = 1$. Keep a count of how many times the instructions in boxes numbers 4 and 7 are repeated.

(d) The second algorithm achieves the same result as the first. Say what you think are the advantages and disadvantages of each.

[MEI, *adapted*]

KEY POINTS

1 An algorithm is a set of instructions used to solve a problem.

2 Algorithms can be communicated in a variety of ways, including flowcharts and text instructions.

3 Bin packing problems are solved using either first fit or first fit decreasing algorithms. Another method, the so-called 'full bin algorithm', is not really an algorithm at all, but depends on the ability of a human to spot efficient combinations.

4 Bubble sort is a simple way of reordering a list into increasing order of size. It can be quite slow, but is easy to use. For a list of $n$ items, a full bubble sort will require $\frac{n(n-1)}{2}$ comparisons to be made.

5 Quick sort, as its name implies, is generally a quicker algorithm for sorting lists, since it repeatedly decomposes the original problem into many smaller, simpler ones. Quick sort is inefficient if the list given is already almost sorted into reverse order.

6 Binary search is a way of locating an object somewhere in a sequential list, by looking at the middle, then in either the first or second half, and so on, until the item is found. The list to be searched is halved in size at each stage, so that $n$ tries are sufficient to guarantee finding the item provided there are no more than $2^n - 1$ items in total (and that the item is in the list).

# Chapter two

# ALGORITHMS ON GRAPHS

It is not down in any map; true places never are.

*Herman Melville*

* * * * * * * * * * * * * *

## NETWORKS

If you have ever travelled on the Underground train system in central London, you will have encountered a diagram similar to the one in figure 2.1.

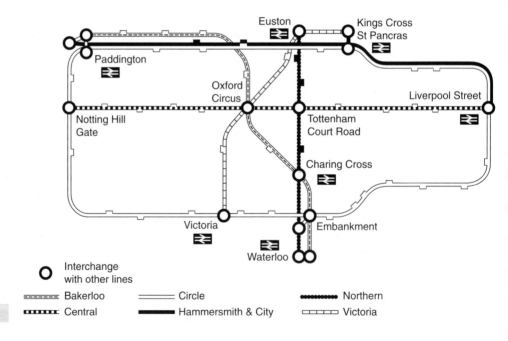

FIGURE 2.1

The diagram shows the Circle line and some of the train lines that intersect with it. Interchanges are marked with circles.

It is tempting to refer to this diagram as 'a map of the underground' (or, at least, part of it), but that would not be strictly correct. The diagram in figure 2.1 is a simplified model of the underground train system which, in reality, looks more like figure 2.2.

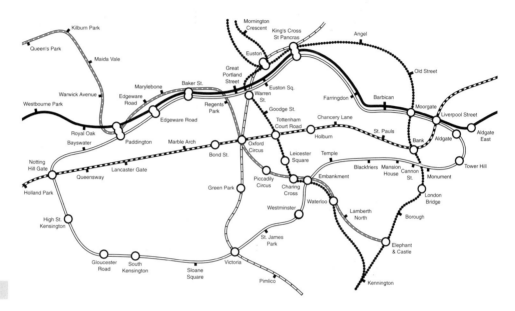

FIGURE 2.2

Here are some of the simplifications that have been made in figure 2.1.

- The train lines have, in general, been drawn as straight as possible.

- The stations have been spaced at regular intervals.

- The intersections have been greatly simplified.

Can you think of any other simplifications?

Underground 'maps' like the one in figure 2.1 were first drawn in the 1930s. All the information about shape and distance on this 'map' turns out to be wrong, but this does not matter at all. The prime purpose of the 'map' is to show how the different stations are connected, so you can see whether it is necessary to change trains to complete your journey.

In this chapter you will be working with diagrams that show how points are connected, but in which the distances are not to scale. Such a diagram is known as a *graph*. If, in addition, there are values marked along the routes, then the graph becomes a *network*.

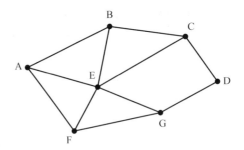

FIGURE 2.3    *A graph*

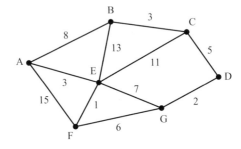

FIGURE 2.4    *A network*

Formally, you say that a *network* is a *weighted graph* – that is, a set of *vertices* (or *nodes*) together with a set of *edges* (or *arcs*). The edges carry *weights*, meaning that there is a numerical value associated with each edge. These may loosely be thought of as 'lengths', but they do not always correspond to distance; they may represent the time taken to travel along an edge or the cost of doing so, for instance.

The terms vertices and nodes are often use interchangeably; so, too, are edges and arcs.

Look again at the graph in figure 2.3. Note that it is not necessary for all the vertices to have direct connections to all the others; for example, there is no direct edge linking E to D.

Such a graph may be described by using an *incidence matrix*; this is simply a table containing zeros when two vertices are not connected and ones when they are.

Here is the incidence matrix for the graph in figure 2.3.

|   | A | B | C | D | E | F | G |
|---|---|---|---|---|---|---|---|
| A | 0 | 1 | 0 | 0 | 1 | 1 | 0 |
| B | 1 | 0 | 1 | 0 | 1 | 0 | 0 |
| C | 0 | 1 | 0 | 1 | 1 | 0 | 0 |
| D | 0 | 0 | 1 | 0 | 0 | 0 | 1 |
| E | 1 | 1 | 1 | 0 | 0 | 1 | 1 |
| F | 1 | 0 | 0 | 0 | 1 | 0 | 1 |
| G | 0 | 0 | 0 | 1 | 1 | 1 | 0 |

Notice that there is a diagonal line of zeros running across the matrix from top left to bottom right. These zeros simply indicate that none of the vertices in figure 2.3 is connected to itself.

Sometimes you can have a vertex connected to itself; the result is a *loop*, as shown in figure 2.5.

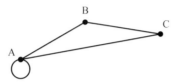

FIGURE 2.5

The existence of a loop is revealed by the appearance of a non-zero value at the corresponding place along the diagonal of the incidence matrix.

# THE MINIMUM CONNECTOR PROBLEM

Look at the network in figure 2.6. Notice that the nodes A and B are connected directly, and they are also connected indirectly by, for example, AE and EB.

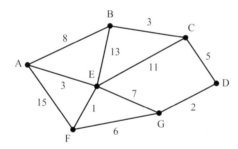

FIGURE 2.6

### ACTIVITY 2.1

Make a copy of the seven nodes of the network shown in figure 2.6, as shown in figure 2.7.

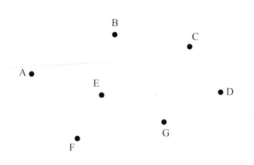

Now try to connect the nodes so that each node forms part of a connected network. You should aim to make the total length of all the arcs as small as possible.

FIGURE 2.7

If you succeeded with Activity 2.1, you will have ended up with a diagram
something like the one in figure 2.8.

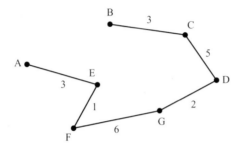

FIGURE 2.8

The total weight of the edges is 3 + 1 + 6 + 2 + 5 + 3 = 20.

In the language of graph theory, a connected set of edges with no loops or cycles is
called a *tree*. The solution shown in figure 2.8 *spans* the network, since it reaches
every node, and it does so using a *minimum* total weight. Hence it is known as a
*minimum connector* or *minimum spanning tree*, sometimes abbreviated to *MST*.

The minimum connector problem is an important one in industrial and commercial
applications, such as connecting towns by road, computers by cable or oil wells by
pipelines. There will usually be too many nodes for the problem to be solved
efficiently by a trial and improvement approach and so a number of algorithms
have been developed to obtain a solution in a systematic way. Two of these are
*Prim's algorithm* and *Kruskal's algorithm* and, while they work in rather different
ways, each of them is guaranteed to find an optimal solution to the problem.

## PRIM'S ALGORITHM

To apply Prim's algorithm, choose a node arbitrarily at which to begin.

Next, look at all the nodes that can be connected to this node by a direct use of an
arc. Select the shortest arc and use it. If there is more than one shortest arc, then
choose arbitrarily.

You now have a set of two nodes connected by an arc. This set will gradually grow,
to evolve into the solution for the minimum connector problem.

Next, look at all the nodes that are not yet connected to the solution set. Pick the
shortest arc and use it, provided it brings a new node into the solution set.

Repeat the previous step as necessary, until $n - 1$ arcs have been used. Then $n$ nodes
have been joined and the minimum connector has been found.

The evolution of the solution to Activity 2.1 is illustrated in figures 2.9 to 2.14. Note that they represent six stages in the development of the solution and, while this book shows them as six separate diagrams for the sake of clarity, you would, in practice, draw the stages on top of each other in a single diagram.

**Step 1**

Start at G (chosen arbitrarily). By referring to the network in figure 2.6, you can see that nodes D, E or F could be connected to G, with weights of 2, 7 or 6 respectively. The smallest of these is 2, so use DG.

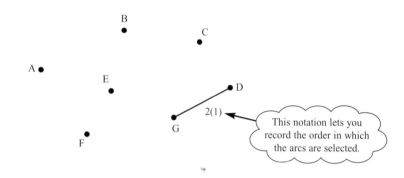

**FIGURE 2.9**

**Step 2**

Nodes C, E or F could be connected to D or G, with weights of 5, 7 or 6 respectively. The smallest of these is 5, so use DC.

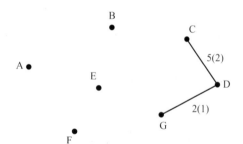

**FIGURE 2.10**

**Step 3**

Nodes B or E could be connected to C with weights of 3 or 11. There are no further arcs available from D. Nodes E or F could be connected to G, with weights of 7 or 6. The smallest weight is 3, so use CB.

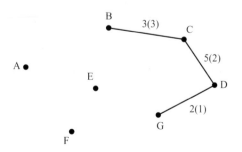

**FIGURE 2.11**

**Step 4**

Nodes A or E could be connected to B, with weights of 8 or 13. Node E could be connected to C or G, with weights of 11 or 7 and Node F could be connected to G, with a weight of 6. The smallest weight is 6, so use GF.

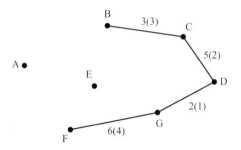

FIGURE 2.12

**Step 5**

Nodes A or E could be connected to B, with weights of 8 or 13. Node E could be connected to C, G or F, with weights of 11, 7 or 1. Node A could be connected to F, with a weight of 15. The smallest weight is 1, so use FE.

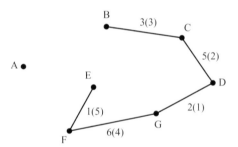

FIGURE 2.13

**Step 6**

Only Node A remains. It could be connected to B, E or F, with weights of 8, 3 or 15. The smallest of these is 3, so use EA.

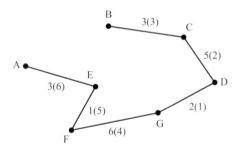

FIGURE 2.14

The final diagram, figure 2.14, shows the minimum connector. Its weight is 3 + 1 + 6 + 2 + 5 + 3 = 20 units.

The arcs have been selected in the order DG, CD, BC, FG, EF, AE.

Although Prim's algorithm works with any node as the start point, some examination questions will tell you where to begin. This is illustrated in the next example.

**EXAMPLE 2.1**

A cable TV company based in Plymouth wishes to make connections in the most economical way to a set of other towns in the south west of England. The towns and their connecting distances (in miles) are marked on the diagram in figure 2.15. Use Prim's algorithm, starting at the company's base, to find a minimum connector. Show clearly the order in which you decided which connections to make.

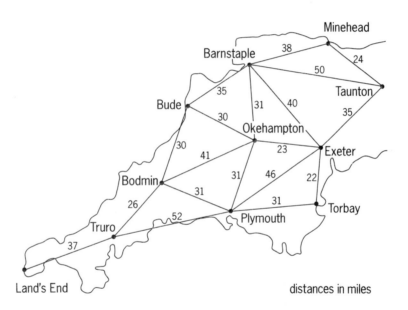

FIGURE 2.15   Land's End                              distances in miles

*Solution*   Taking Plymouth as the starting point, the first arc to be selected could be any of the three of weight 31, from Plymouth to Bodmin, Okehampton or Torbay. Arbitrarily choose Plymouth to Torbay, and mark this on the solution diagram in figure 2.16 as 31(1). Continuing to apply Prim's algorithm, you end up with the full solution shown in figure 2.16.

The length of the minimum connector is

31 + 22 + 23 + 31 + 30 + 30 + 26 + 37 + 35 + 24 = 289 miles.

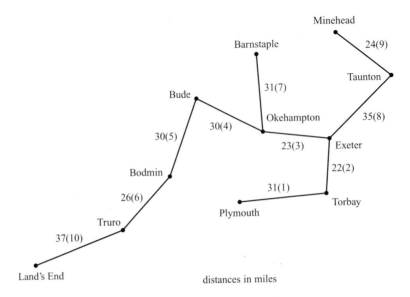

FIGURE 2.16    distances in miles

EXERCISE 2A    1 The diagram shows a network with various connections.

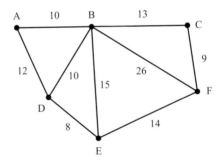

(a) Calculate the total length of all the connections given in the diagram.

(b) Use Prim's algorithm, starting at D, to find a minimum spanning tree, and give its length.

(c) Express the length of the minimum connector as a percentage of the total length of all of the original connections.

**2** Use Prim's algorithm to find a minimum connector for each of the networks below. Calculate the length of the minimum connector in each case. Weights indicate distances in miles.

**(a)**

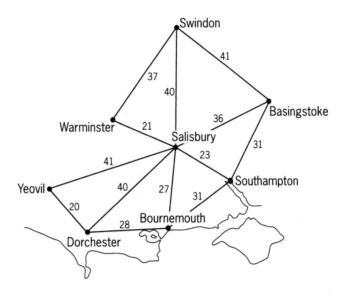

**(b)**

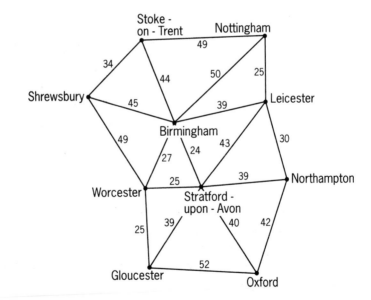

(c)

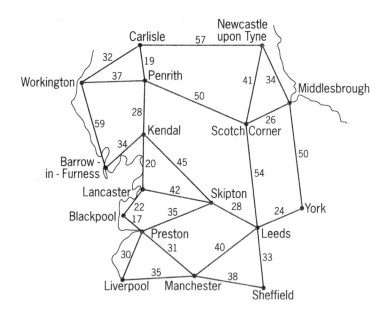

(d)

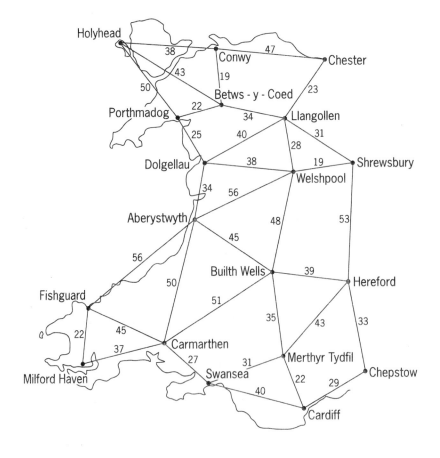

## PRIM'S ALGORITHM IN MATRIX FORM

Prim's algorithm may also be applied to a network given in the form of a table. Consider again the network in figure 2.6, repeated here as in figure 2.17.

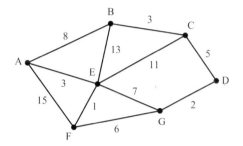

FIGURE 2.17

The information in the network could have been presented in a table, as here. This is known as a *matrix*.

|   | A | B | C | D | E | F | G |
|---|---|---|---|---|---|---|---|
| A | – | 8 | – | – | 3 | 15 | – |
| B | 8 | – | 3 | – | 13 | – | – |
| C | – | 3 | – | 5 | 11 | – | – |
| D | – | – | 5 | – | – | – | 2 |
| E | 3 | 13 | 11 | – | – | 1 | 7 |
| F | 15 | – | – | – | 1 | – | 6 |
| G | – | – | – | 2 | 7 | 6 | – |

To begin to apply Prim's algorithm, you need a start node. Sometimes a question will specify this node but, if not, you simply choose a node arbitrarily. For this example D is chosen as the start node.

Now circle the D at the top of the matrix and cross out the row corresponding to D, as shown here.

Record the order in which nodes are selected.

|   | A | B | C | (D)¹ | E | F | G |
|---|---|---|---|---|---|---|---|
| A | – | 8 | – | – | 3 | 15 | – |
| B | 8 | – | 3 | – | 13 | – | – |
| C | – | 3 | – | 5 | 11 | – | – |
| D | = | = | 5 | = | = | = | 2 |
| E | 3 | 13 | 11 | – | – | 1 | 7 |
| F | 15 | – | – | – | 1 | – | 6 |
| G | – | – | – | 2 | 7 | 6 | – |

Now look down the D column and identify the smallest arc. (In the event of a tie, choose arbitrarily). In this case it is 2, which connects with G. So, circle the value of 2, and bring G into the solution by circling G in the header row and crossing out row G as shown below.

|   | A | B | C | (D)¹ | E | F | (G)² |
|---|---|---|---|---|---|---|---|
| A | – | 8 | – | – | 3 | 15 | – |
| B | 8 | – | 3 | – | 13 | – | – |
| C | – | 3 | – | 5 | 11 | – | – |
| ~~D~~ | ~~–~~ | ~~–~~ | ~~5~~ | ~~–~~ | ~~–~~ | ~~–~~ | ~~2~~ |
| E | 3 | 13 | 11 | – | – | 1 | 7 |
| F | 15 | – | – | – | 1 | – | 6 |
| ~~G~~ | ~~–~~ | ~~–~~ | ~~–~~ | (2) | ~~7~~ | ~~6~~ | ~~–~~ |

Continue by looking down *all* the selected columns, D and G at present, to identify the shortest arc. The values are 5, 7 and 6, so choose 5, connecting D and C. C now joins the solution set.

|   | A | B | (C)³ | (D)¹ | E | F | (G)² |
|---|---|---|---|---|---|---|---|
| A | – | 8 | – | – | 3 | 15 | – |
| B | 8 | – | 3 | – | 13 | – | – |
| ~~C~~ | ~~–~~ | ~~3~~ | ~~–~~ | (5) | ~~11~~ | ~~–~~ | ~~–~~ |
| ~~D~~ | ~~–~~ | ~~–~~ | ~~5~~ | ~~–~~ | ~~–~~ | ~~–~~ | ~~2~~ |
| E | 3 | 13 | 11 | – | – | 1 | 7 |
| F | 15 | – | – | – | 1 | – | 6 |
| ~~G~~ | ~~–~~ | ~~–~~ | ~~–~~ | (2) | ~~7~~ | ~~6~~ | ~~–~~ |

Scanning the columns for C, D and G, the next value to use is 3, corresponding to the arc CB. Thus B now joins the solution set.

| | A | B ⁴ | C ³ | D ¹ | E | F | G ² |
|---|---|---|---|---|---|---|---|
| A | – | 8 | – | – | 3 | 15 | – |
| B | 8 | – | 3 | – | 13 | – | – |
| C | – | 3 | – | 5 | 11 | – | – |
| D | – | – | 5 | – | – | – | 2 |
| E | 3 | 13 | 11 | – | – | 1 | 7 |
| F | 15 | – | – | – | 1 | – | 6 |
| G | – | – | – | 2 | 7 | 6 | – |

Scanning the columns for B, C, D and G, the next value to use is 6, corresponding to the arc GF. Thus F now joins the solution set.

| | A | B ⁴ | C ³ | D ¹ | E | F ⁵ | G ² |
|---|---|---|---|---|---|---|---|
| A | – | 8 | – | – | 3 | 15 | – |
| B | 8 | – | 3 | – | 13 | – | – |
| C | – | 3 | – | 5 | 11 | – | – |
| D | – | – | 5 | – | – | – | 2 |
| E | 3 | 13 | 11 | – | – | 1 | 7 |
| F | 15 | – | – | – | 1 | – | 6 |
| G | – | – | – | 2 | 7 | 6 | – |

Scanning the columns for B, C, D, F and G, the next value to use is 1, corresponding to the arc FE. Thus E now joins the solution set.

| | A | B ⁴ | C ³ | D ¹ | E ⁶ | F ⁵ | G ² |
|---|---|---|---|---|---|---|---|
| A | – | 8 | – | – | 3 | 15 | – |
| B | 8 | – | 3 | – | 13 | – | – |
| C | – | 3 | – | 5 | 11 | – | – |
| D | – | – | 5 | – | – | – | 2 |
| E | 3 | 13 | 11 | – | – | 1 | 7 |
| F | 15 | – | – | – | 1 | – | 6 |
| G | – | – | – | 2 | 7 | 6 | – |

Finally, scanning the columns for B, C, D, E, F and G yields a value of 3, corresponding to the arc EA. Thus A now joins the solution set and the nodes are all connected.

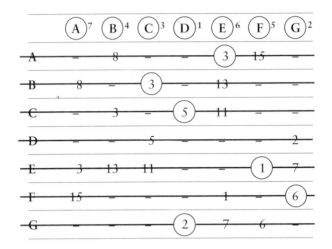

To obtain the solution, you simply extract the circled values from the table. In the order they were selected, we have:

DG: 2

DC: 5

CB: 3

GF: 6

FE: 1

EA: 3

The total length is then 2 + 5 + 3 + 6 + 1 + 3 = 20.

**Note**            For the exam you will be asked to list the arcs in the order you chose them.

Note that this solution is identical to the one obtained, for the same problem, on page 29 using the graphical form of Prim's algorithm.

The real strength of the matrix form of Prim's algorithm lies in the fact that it is easily programmable and thus well suited to networks containing a large number of nodes.

EXERCISE 2B    *Use the matrix form of Prim's algorithm to find a minimum connector for each of these networks. Calculate the length of the minimum connector in each case. Distances are given in miles.*

**1 (a)**

|  | Malvern | Worcester | Hereford | Evesham | Ross | Tewkesbury | Gloucester | Cheltenham |
|---|---|---|---|---|---|---|---|---|
| Malvern | – | 8 | 19 | – | 19 | 13 | 20 | – |
| Worcester | 8 | – | 25 | 16 | – | 15 | – | – |
| Hereford | 19 | 25 | – | – | 14 | – | 28 | – |
| Evesham | – | 16 | – | – | – | 13 | – | 16 |
| Ross | 19 | – | 14 | – | – | 24 | 16 | – |
| Tewkesbury | 13 | 15 | – | 13 | 24 | – | 10 | 9 |
| Gloucester | 20 | – | 28 | – | 16 | 10 | – | 9 |
| Cheltenham | – | – | – | 16 | – | 9 | 9 | – |

**(b)**

|  | Dorchester | Puddletown | Blandford | Wimborne | Bere Regis | Lytchett Minster | Weymouth | Warmwell | Wareham | Swanage | Poole |
|---|---|---|---|---|---|---|---|---|---|---|---|
| Dorchester | – | 5 | – | – | – | – | 8 | 5 | – | – | – |
| Puddletown | 5 | – | 12 | – | 6 | – | – | 9 | 14 | – | – |
| Blandford | – | 12 | – | 7 | 9 | 11 | – | – | 16 | – | – |
| Wimborne | – | – | 7 | – | 8 | 7 | – | – | – | – | 7 |
| Bere Regis | – | 6 | 9 | 8 | – | 8 | 19 | 11 | 8 | – | – |
| Lytchett Minster | – | – | 11 | 7 | 8 | – | 25 | – | 5 | – | 6 |
| Weymouth | 8 | – | – | – | 19 | 25 | – | 7 | – | – | – |
| Warmwell | 5 | 9 | – | – | 11 | – | 7 | – | 13 | – | – |
| Wareham | – | 14 | 16 | – | 8 | 5 | – | 13 | – | 10 | – |
| Swanage | – | – | – | – | – | – | – | – | 10 | – | – |
| Poole | – | – | – | 7 | – | 6 | – | – | – | – | – |

2  The table below shows the distances by road, in kilometres, between six small towns.

|   | A | B | C | D | E | F |
|---|---|---|---|---|---|---|
| A | – | 20 | 12 | 4 | – | – |
| B | 20 | – | 6 | 19 | – | – |
| C | 12 | 6 | – | 15 | – | 6 |
| D | 4 | 19 | 15 | – | 9 | – |
| E | – | – | – | 9 | – | 12 |
| F | – | – | 6 | – | 12 | – |

(a) Starting with node A, use Prim's algorithm in matrix form to find a minimum connector. Name the edges used to form your minimum connector and give its total value.

(b) Illustrate your solution with a suitable diagram.

(c) Is your solution unique?

## KRUSKAL'S ALGORITHM

There is an alternative algorithm for finding a minimum connector. Kruskal's algorithm depends on sorting the available arcs into increasing order of size. The smallest arc is used to begin with. Then each next arc is examined, in order of size, and is selected provided it does not complete a cycle; otherwise, it is rejected. The algorithm continues until $n - 1$ arcs have been selected; this guarantees that the $n$ nodes will be connected.

When working through the arcs in order of size, it is possible that two or more might have the same weight. In such cases simply choose arbitrarily which of them to consider next.

Kruskal's algorithm is a perfectly logical and straightforward method for solving small networks by hand but it becomes cumbersome for large ones. Also, it is far less easy to program than Prim's algorithm. Your examination specification does, however, require that you are able to use both methods.

## EXAMPLE 2.2

Use Kruskal's algorithm to find a minimum connector for the network in figure 2.18.

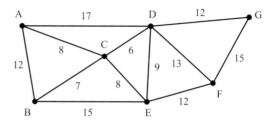

FIGURE 2.18

*Solution*

The arcs, in increasing order of size, are given in the table.

| Weight | Arc |
|--------|-----|
| 6 | CD |
| 7 | BC |
| 8 | AC, CE |
| 9 | DE |
| 12 | AB, DG, EF |
| 13 | DF |
| 15 | BE, FG |
| 17 | AD |

To begin with, use CD, then BC, then both AC and CE, since each time a new node is added, to obtain the partial solution shown in figure 2.19.

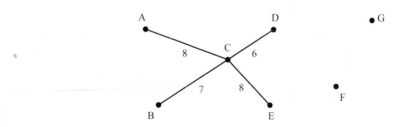

FIGURE 2.19

The next arc to be considered is DE, of length 9. This arc is discarded, since it does not add any new node, it merely closes a circuit DCE. Such a closed circuit is known as a *cycle*. Similarly, the arc AB of length 12 is also not used.

The arc DG, of length 12, is used, since it adds G into the solution network. Next, arc EF, also of length 12, is used, as this adds F.

All nodes are now in the network, so the minimum spanning tree is complete. There are seven nodes, so 7 – 1 = 6 arcs have been used.

The solution is shown in figure 2.20.

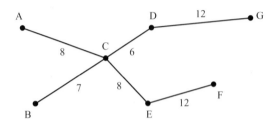

FIGURE 2.20

The total weight of the solution is 8 + 7 + 6 + 8 + 12 + 12 = 53 units.

Note that in an examination question you would draw all the various stages in a single diagram. In order to let the examiner see the order in which you added the arcs, sequential numbers can be added in brackets, so your solution would look as shown in figure 2.21.

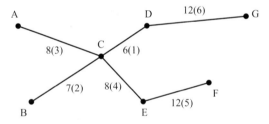

FIGURE 2.21

**Note**

In the exam you will be required to state the order in which you chose the arcs and at which point you decided to reject any arcs. For example, CD, BC, AC, CE, not DE, not AB, EF, DG, stop.

EXERCISE 2C

**1** Use Kruskal's algorithm to find a minimum connector for each of these networks. Calculate the length of your minimum connector in each case.

**(a)**

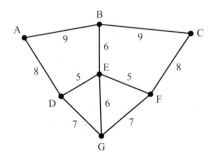

**(b)**

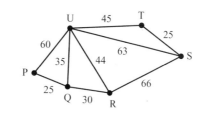

**(c)**

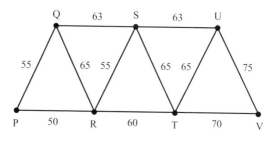

**(d)**

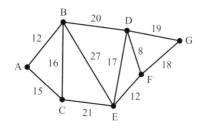

2  Modern Electronic Instruments Ltd has seven depots. The distances between them, in miles, by direct road links are shown in the diagram.

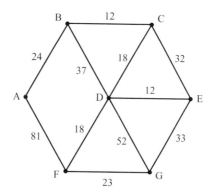

**(a)**  Communication cables are to be laid along these roads so that all depots are linked by cable, either directly or via other depots. Use Kruskal's algorithm to find the minimum length of cable that is required. List the order in which the roads are chosen for cabling.

An eighth depot is established at H. The new depot is connected directly by roads to A, B and E, with distances of 6, 17 and 54 miles respectively.

**(b)**  Starting from your solution to part **(a)**, find the minimum length of cable needed to link the extended network.

[MEI, *part*]

# THE SHORTEST DISTANCE PROBLEM

This section examines the problem of finding the *shortest route* between two nodes in a network.

Consider the network shown in figure 2.22. The aim is to find the shortest route from S to T.

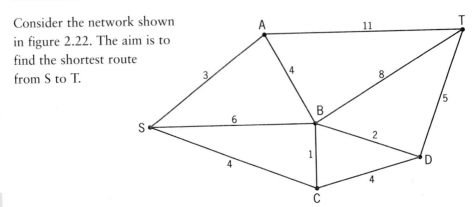

FIGURE 2.22

Try to find the shortest route from S to T by inspection.
How can you be sure that your solution really is the shortest route?

Although it is not hard to find a short route through this network by inspection, there will be a nagging doubt as to whether it really is the shortest possible route. Furthermore, as the number of nodes increases, the problem soon becomes too difficult to solve simply by inspection. A formal algorithm is needed and the standard one that is used was devised by Dijkstra (pronounced *dike'-stra*).

## DIJKSTRA'S ALGORITHM

To apply Dijkstra's algorithm, you begin by looking at all the nodes that can be reached directly from the starting node. Assign each of them a *temporary label* consisting of a working value that shows the weight required to reach that node in one step. You then take the smallest temporary label and make it *permanent*, so its value is now final. So, to the network in figure 2.22 you assign the temporary labels at A (3), B (6) and C (4). You then make the value 3 at A permanent.

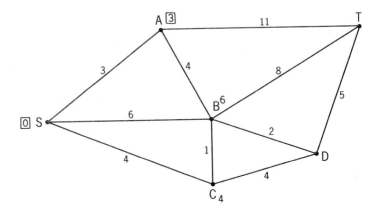

FIGURE 2.23

Now using A as a start point, you assign temporary labels to all the nodes that may be reached in one step from A. If a node already has a pre-existing temporary label, then you replace it with the new value only if it is lower. So, T takes a temporary label of 14; B would be 7 but as there is already a value of 6 you do not replace it with 7.

Next, examine all the temporary labels and make the smallest one permanent. This will be C (4).

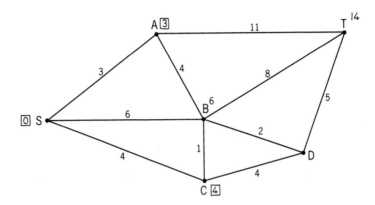

FIGURE 2.24

You continue the process from C. Note now that B can have a temporary label of 5, from 4 + 1 via SC and CB and, since this is lower than the pre-existing value of 6, you lightly cross out 6 and replace it with 5, taking care to ensure that the original value of 6 is clearly visible under the crossing out. D takes a temporary label of 8.

Once again, examine all the temporary labels and make the smallest one permanent. This time it is B (5).

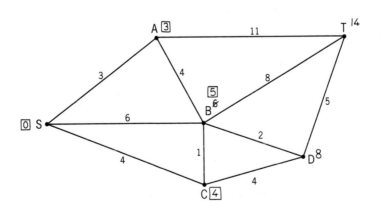

FIGURE 2.25

Continuing from B, you obtain reduced values at T, of 13, and at D, of 7, and D becomes the next node to gain a permanent label.

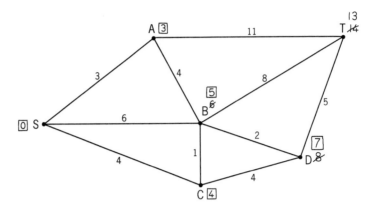

FIGURE 2.26

Now starting from D, the temporary label at T reduces to 7 + 5 = 12 since this is lower than the previous value of 13. This becomes the next permanent label and, since all the nodes have been labelled permanently, the algorithm now stops. The shortest distance from S to T is the permanent label at T, which is 12.

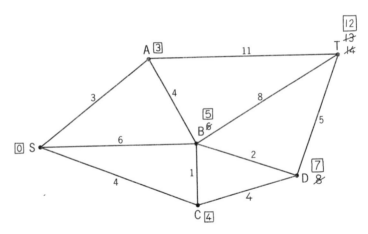

FIGURE 2.27

To extract the route that leads to 12, you work backwards from T.

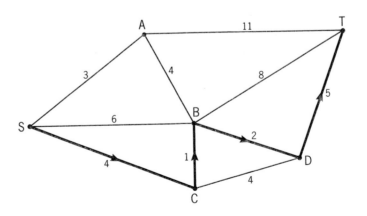

FIGURE 2.28

TD is used since $12 - 7 = 5$.

Then from D,

DB is used since $7 - 5 = 2$.

Then from B,

BC is used since $5 - 4 = 1$.

Finally, from C,

CS is used since $4 - 0 = 4$.

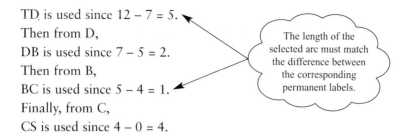

The length of the selected arc must match the difference between the corresponding permanent labels.

So the shortest route is SCBDT, with a total weight of 12.

To improve clarity, it is customary to have boxes at each node. The boxes are made up of three parts.

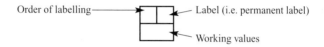

Order of labelling ——— Label (i.e. permanent label)

Working values

Using this notation, the solution to the problem above is as shown in figure 2.29.

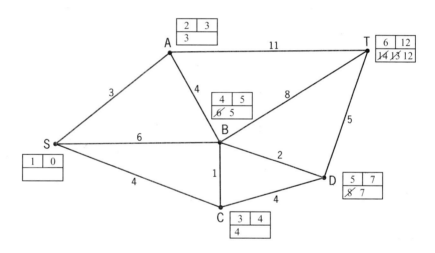

**FIGURE 2.29**

Notice how the working values can be updated whilst leaving the earlier values legible. This gives evidence that you are applying the algorithm correctly. Also, an examiner can check that you have made your permanent node decisions in the right order. In the diagram above the nodes have been ordered 1, 2, 3, 4, 5, 6 but it would be equally valid to have labelled them 0, 1, 2, 3, 4, 5 – it is simply a matter of personal preference.

EXERCISE 2D

**1** Use Dijkstra's algorithm to find a shortest path from S to T for each of these networks. Remember to draw suitable boxes at each node when you prepare your solution diagram.

**(a)**

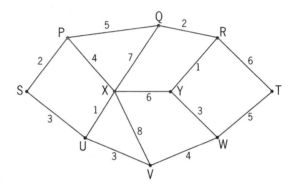

**(b)**

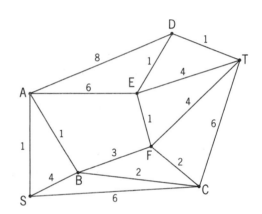

**(c)**

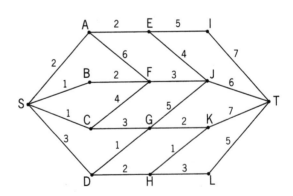

2 The map below shows the main railway lines across the USA and gives the approximate times in hours for the various journeys.

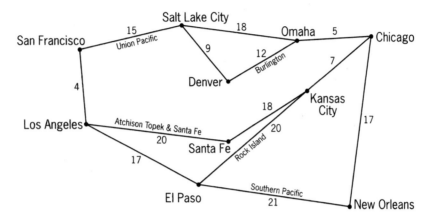

(a) Find the quickest route from Los Angeles to Chicago.

(b) Find the quickest route from New Orleans to Denver.

(c) If you can travel by road from El Paso to Santa Fe in 5 hours and from Santa Fe to Denver in 5 hours, would you save time on the journeys in parts (a) and (b) by using a mix of road and rail? (You should neglect connection times.)

3 The fire department in Westingham has a team fighting a large blaze at one of the town's hotels. They urgently need help from one of the neighbouring towns, A, B or C. The estimated times (in minutes) to travel along the various sections of road from A, B and C to Westingham are shown on the network below. Which town's fire fighters should they call upon and how long will it take them to travel to the fire?

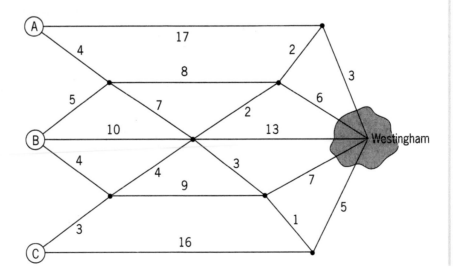

**4** The weights on the network in the diagram represent distances.

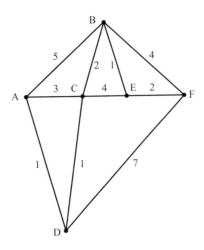

(a) Apply Dijkstra's algorithm to find the shortest route from A to F.

(b) Give the shortest route and its length.

[MEI]

## DEFINITIONS IN GRAPH THEORY

The following definitions are often used in graph theory, and you need to be familiar with all of them. Some of them have already been introduced earlier in the chapter, while others are probably new to you.

Once you have read and understood these definitions you will need to learn them. You should then be ready to tackle the questions in Exercise 2E.

- A *graph* G consists of points (*vertices* or *nodes*) that are connected by lines (*edges* or *arcs*). If the edges have corresponding values (*weights*), then the graph is known as a *network*.

- A *subgraph* of G is a graph made up using some of the edges and vertices of G.

- The *degree* or *valency* or *order* of a node is the number of edges meeting at that node. A node is *odd* if it has an odd degree and *even* if it has an even degree.

Order 3          Order 4          Order 4 including loop

**FIGURE 2.30**

- A *loop* is an edge with both ends connected to the same vertex.

- A *path* is a finite sequence of edges, such that the end node of one edge is the start node of the next. Each node is used at most once.

FIGURE 2.31    *A path*

- A *cycle* or *circuit* is a closed path; the last node in the path is joined to the first. Be careful not to call this a loop by mistake (see figure 2.30 above).

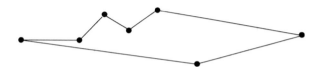

FIGURE 2.32    *A cycle*

- A cycle that passes through every node of a graph is called a *Hamiltonian cycle* and a graph that contains a Hamiltonian cycle is said to be *Hamiltonian*.

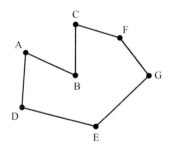

FIGURE 2.33    *A Hamiltonian cycle*

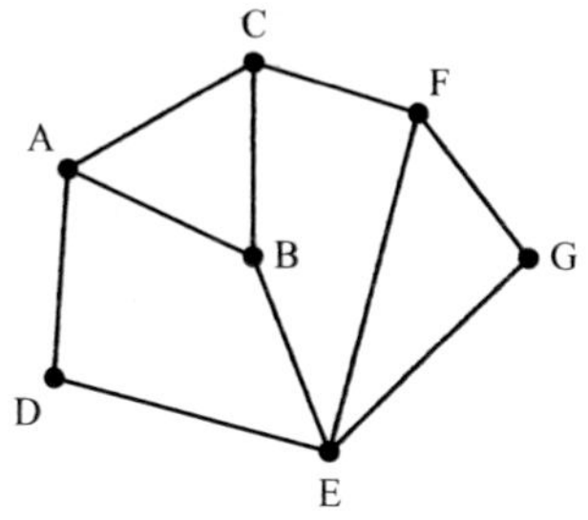

FIGURE 2.34    *A Hamiltonian graph*

- Two vertices are *connected* if there is a path between them; a graph is connected if all its vertices are connected.

- If the edges of a graph have a direction associated with them they are known as *directed edges* and the graph is known as a *digraph* (= *di*(rected) + *graph*).

FIGURE 2.35    *A directed edge*

A *tree* is a connected graph with no cycles.

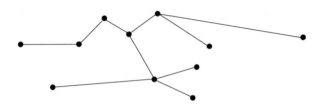

FIGURE 2.36    *A tree*

- A tree which includes all the vertices of a graph is called a *spanning tree*.

- A *minimum spanning tree* (MST) is a spanning tree such that the total weight of its edges is as small as possible. (This is sometimes called a *minimum connector*.)

- A graph in which each of the *n* vertices is connected to every other vertex is called a *complete graph*. (The notation $K_n$ is used for such a graph with *n* vertices).

- A graph is *planar* if it can be drawn on a plane in such a way that no two edges cross each other.

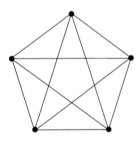

FIGURE 2.37    *The complete graph with five vertices, $K_5$*

*Questions 1 to 8 refer to the nine diagrams A to I opposite.*

1 Which one is a network?

2 Which are trees?

3 Which ones are connected?

4 Which one contains a loop?

5 Which ones are complete?

6 Which ones are planar? [Be careful here!]

7 Which ones contain a Hamiltonian cycle as a subgraph?

8 Which one is a digraph?

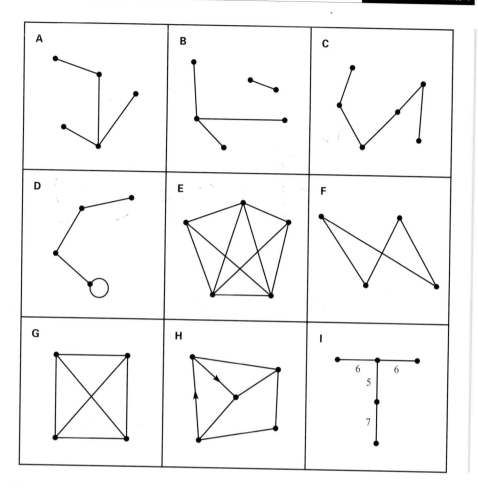

# PLANAR AND NON-PLANAR GRAPHS

If a graph is planar, then it must be possible to redraw it on a plane so that none of the edges cross each other.

**EXAMPLE 2.3**

Show that this graph is planar.

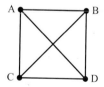

FIGURE 2.38

*Solution*   Since you are told that the graph is planar, you need to find a way of redrawing it so that the edges AD and BC do not cross. This can be achieved by simply rerouting the connection AD to go around the 'outside' as shown in figure 2.39.

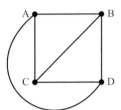

**FIGURE 2.39**

Now look at Example 2.3 in a different way. You could begin by drawing the Hamiltonian cycle ABDCA:

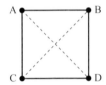

**FIGURE 2.40**

So far, you have managed to draw a subgraph of the original graph. The edges AD and BC remain to be added. They appear to cross each other but, since there are only two of them, you can draw one around the *outside* of the Hamiltonian cycle ABDCA and the other one *within* the cycle. Thus the graph can be redrawn without any edges crossing, so it meets the definition of being planar.

### THE PLANARITY ALGORITHM

- Examine the given graph and identify a Hamiltonian cycle.

- Draw this cycle flat on the plane.

- Then, if the remaining connections require three or more edges (using vertices of the cycle) that cross each other, then the graph must be non-planar.

- If, instead, at most two such edges cross each other, then the graph is planar.

**EXAMPLE 2.4**

Prove that $K_6$, the complete graph with six vertices, is non-planar.

*Solution*

The graph of $K_6$ may be drawn as shown in figure 2.41.

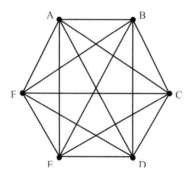

FIGURE 2.41

Now pick out the Hamiltonian cycle ABCDEF, and lay it out on the plane as shown in figure 2.42.

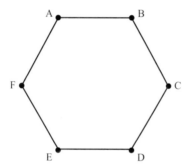

FIGURE 2.42

In order to complete the graph it is necessary, at some stage, to use AD, BE and FC. These three edges all cross each other, as shown in figure 2.43.

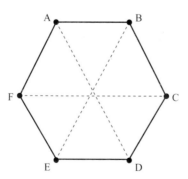

FIGURE 2.43

There are three of these, therefore, by the planarity algorithm, $K_6$ is non-planar.

Two well-known examples of non-planar graphs are $K_5$ and $K_{3,3}$. $K_5$ is the complete graph formed by connecting five vertices to each other; $K_{3,3}$ is the complete bipartite graph (to be encountered again, more fully, in Chapter 6) formed using two sets of three vertices. These graphs are shown below.

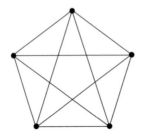

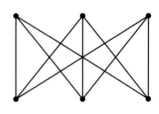

FIGURE 2.44    *The graph $K_5$*                    FIGURE 2.45    *The graph $K_{3,3}$*

Your specification requires you to *know* that $K_5$ and $K_{3,3}$ are non-planar, and you should also know how to *prove* these, using the planarity algorithm.

EXERCISE 2F

**1** The diagram shows six vertices A, B, C, P, Q and R together with a set of edges.

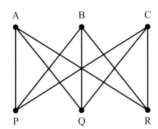

(a) Notice that it is possible to make a path using the edges AP, PB, BQ, QC, CR and RA. What name is given to such a path?

(b) Make a sketch of this path, by arranging the vertices A, P, B, Q, C and R (in that order) as the vertices of a hexagon.

(c) Now add lines to your diagram to show the three remaining edges from the original diagram. Hence use the planarity algorithm to explain whether or not this graph is planar.

**2** Use the planarity algorithm to show that the complete graph $K_5$, shown here, is non-planar.

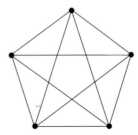

3 The diagram below shows three houses, $H_1$, $H_2$ and $H_3$, and three services G (gas), W (water) and E (electricity). An engineer wants to connect each service to each house, but does not want any of the connections to cross over each other.

(a) Explain briefly why the engineer's wish is impossible to achieve.

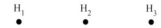

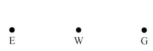

(b) Can the engineer succeed in connecting *four* houses to *two* services?

4 Look at the graph below.

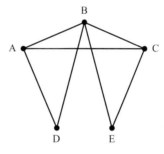

(a) Show that this graph is planar.
(b) State the pairs of vertices that need to be joined in order to form a complete graph.
(c) Explain briefly how you can tell whether this complete graph is planar or non-planar.

5 (a) Use the planarity algorithm to show that this graph is planar.

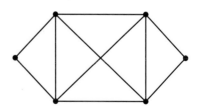

(b) Use the planarity algorithm to show that this graph is not planar.

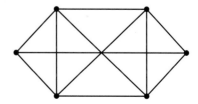

EXERCISE 2G  EXAMINATION-STYLE QUESTIONS

1  Use Prim's algorithm, starting at A, to find a minimum connector for the
   following network. Record the order in which you select the arcs and give the
   total weight of your solution.

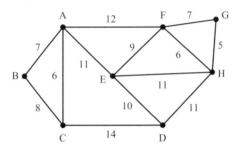

2  Use the matrix form of Prim's algorithm, starting at A, to find a minimum
   connector for the network defined by the arc weights given in the table.

|   | A | B | C | D | E |
|---|---|---|---|---|---|
| A | – | 12 | 8 | 7 | 9 |
| B | 12 | – | 10 | – | 9 |
| C | 8 | 10 | – | 4 | 5 |
| D | 7 | – | 4 | – | 3 |
| E | 9 | 9 | 5 | 3 | – |

Draw your minimum connector and
give its total weight.

[MEI]

3  The diagram shows seven locations, A, B, C, D, E, F and G, which are to be
   connected by pipelines. The arcs show the possible routes. The number on each
   arc gives the cost, in thousands of pounds, of laying that particular section.

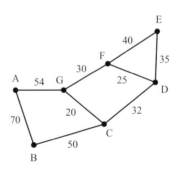

   (a)  Use Kruskal's algorithm to obtain a minimum spanning tree for the
        network, giving the order in which you selected the arcs.
   (b)  Draw your minimum spanning tree and find the least cost of pipelines.

[Edexcel]

**4** A school wishes to link six computers. One is in the school office and one in each of the rooms A, B, C, D and E. Cables need to be laid to connect the computers. The school wishes to use a minimum total length of cable.

The table shows the shortest distances, in metres, between the various sites.

|  | Office | Room A | Room B | Room C | Room D | Room E |
|---|---|---|---|---|---|---|
| Office | – | 8 | 16 | 12 | 10 | 14 |
| Room A | 8 | – | 14 | 13 | 11 | 9 |
| Room B | 16 | 14 | – | 12 | 15 | 11 |
| Room C | 12 | 13 | 12 | – | 11 | 8 |
| Room D | 10 | 22 | 15 | 11 | – | 10 |
| Room E | 14 | 9 | 11 | 8 | 10 | – |

(a) Starting at the school office, use Prim's algorithm to find a minimum spanning tree. Indicate the order in which you select the edges and draw your final tree.

(b) Using your answer to part (a), calculate the minimum total length of cable required.

[Edexcel]

**5** A student is solving a minimum connector problem in an examination. The diagram below shows the problem and the student's (correct) partially completed solution.

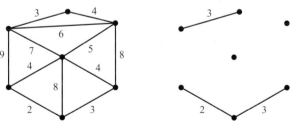

*Original problem*                 *Partial solution*

(a) Explain how you can tell whether the student has been using Prim's algorithm or Kruskal's algorithm.

(b) Copy the student's partial solution and complete it. Write down the total weight of the minimum connector.

**6** The diagram represents the roads joining ten villages, labelled A to J.
The numbers give distances in kilometres.

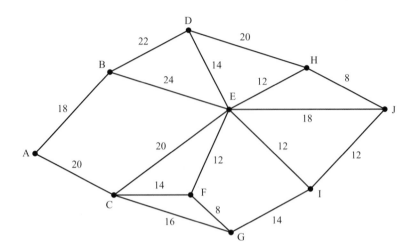

(a) Use Dijkstra's algorithm to find a shortest route from A to J. Explain the
method carefully, and show all of your working. Give your shortest route
and its length.

A driver usually completes this journey driving at 60 km h$^{-1}$. The local radio
reports a serious fire at village E, and warns drivers of a delay of 10 minutes.

(b) Describe how to modify your approach to part (a) to find the quickest
route, explaining how to take account of this information. What is the
quickest route, and how long will it take?

[Oxford] Please note that this question is NOT from
the live examinations for the current specification

**7** The weighted network below models the area in which Bill lives. Each node represents a town. The arcs represent the roads between towns. The weights are the lengths, in kilometres, of the roads.

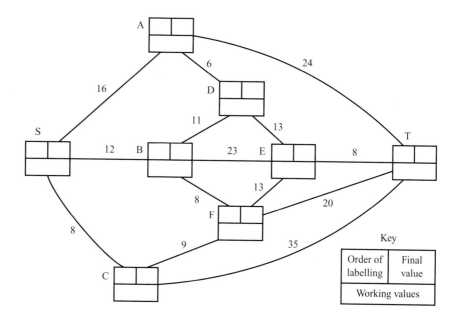

(a) Use Dijkstra's algorithm to find the shortest route from Bill's home at S to T. Explain clearly how you determined the path of least weight from your labelling.

Bill decides that on the way to T he must visit a shop in town E.

(b) Obtain his shortest route now, giving its length and explaining your method clearly.

[Edexcel]

**8** The network represents a number of villages together with connecting roads. The numbers on the arcs represent distances in miles.

(a) Use Dijkstra's algorithm to find the shortest routes from A to each of the other villages.

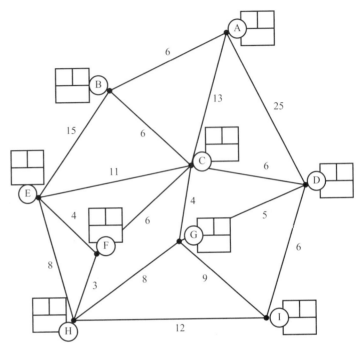

(b) As part of a traffic management scheme it is proposed to turn the road connecting C and G into a one-way road, traffic only being allowed to proceed in the direction from G to C. What differences would this make to your shortest routes and distances?

(c) In protest at the proposals in part (b), and before they are implemented, a group of road users stage a demonstration in the centre of C which delays all traffic passing through C by 20 minutes.

  (i) Given that traffic in the area travels at 30 mph, explain how to adapt the network to model this information so that an application of Dijkstra's algorithm will produce the fastest journey *time* from A to F.

  (ii) Find the fastest route from A to F during the demonstration.
  
  [MEI]

**9 (a)** The network opposite consists of a set of nodes and connecting arcs. Each arc has a number (or *weight*) associated with it.

  Use Dijkstra's algorithm to find the 'shortest' route from L to A in this network, i.e. the route such that the sum of the weights on the arcs is as small as possible.

  (Record the order in which you permanently label nodes, and write your working values and final values in boxes at the vertices.)

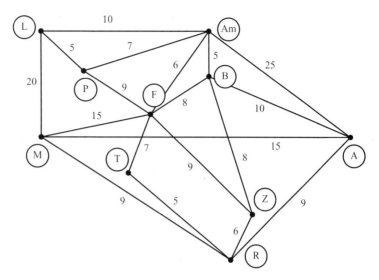

(b) In fact the nodes of the network represent European cities, and the arcs represent air freight routes flown by a particular company. The company has a plane in London (L), which it needs to fly to Athens (A) to collect a contracted load. The weights on the arcs are the profits (£100s) which the company can make by moving loads from city to city en route. The profits are only available in the directions indicated in the diagram below. Company policy is that the plane should fly only along routes where loads are available.

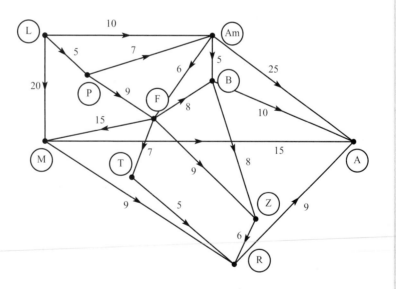

(i) Say how this problem differs from the problem in part (a).

(ii) Describe how Dijkstra's algorithm could be adapted to solve this problem.

[MEI]

10  The diagram shows a printed circuit board with two points for external
    connection and three internal points. Each of the connection points is to be
    wired to each of the internal points.

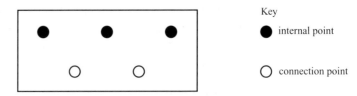

Key

● internal point

○ connection point

(a)  Show that the two connection points can be wired directly to each of the
     three internal points without any wires crossing.
(b)  Show that two connection points can be wired to four internal points
     without any wires crossing.
(c)  Give the smallest numbers of connection points and internal points for
     which at least one crossing will be required.

[MEI]

## KEY POINTS

1  A *graph* consists of *vertices* or *nodes* connected by *edges* or *arcs*. A graph with
   *weights* is called a *network*.

2  A *connected graph* has no separate *vertices*. A *simple graph* has no loops and
   not more than one edge connecting any pair of vertices.

3  The *degree* or *valency* or *order* of a vertex is the number of edges converging
   on it.

4  A *cycle* is a closed path; the end of one edge is the start of the next.

5  A *Hamiltonian cycle* is a cycle that passes through every vertex of a graph.

6  If an edge of a graph has a direction associated with it, it is a *directed edge*; the
   graph is then a *digraph*.

7  A *tree* is a connected graph with no cycles.

8  A *minimum spanning tree* is a tree that includes all the nodes of a network,
   and does so in such a way that the total weight of the corresponding arcs is
   a minimum.

9  A graph in which every vertex is connected to every other one is called a
   *complete graph*.

10 A *planar graph* is one which may be drawn on a flat plane without any edges crossing.

11 *Prim's algorithm* is used for finding a minimum connector. It repeatedly adds new nodes to a connected set by looking for a new node that is 'closest' to the connected set. Prim's algorithm may be implemented in both graphical and matrix form.

12 *Kruskal's* algorithm is also used for finding a minimum connector. The smallest arcs are used first, then larger ones. An arc must not be used if it completes a cycle.

13 *Dijkstra's* algorithm is used for finding a shortest route. At each iteration, the node with the smallest temporary label is made permanent, and the set of temporary labels is updated based on (one-stage) distances from the new permanent label. This is repeated until the destination vertex is permanently labelled.

14 *The planarity algorithm* can be used if a graph contains a Hamiltonian cycle. First draw that cycle flat on the plane. If the original graph requires three or more further edges, which all cross each other, then the graph must be non-planar.

# Chapter three

# THE ROUTE INSPECTION PROBLEM

The postman always rings twice.

*James M Cain*

● ● ● ● ● ● ● ● ● ● ● ● ● ● ●

## TRAVERSABILITY

There is a legendary mathematical puzzle about the city of Königsberg. It goes like this.

*The citizens of 18th-century Königsberg liked to walk around the various parts of their city on Sundays. They wished to cross over each bridge exactly once, returning to their starting point at the end of the walk.*

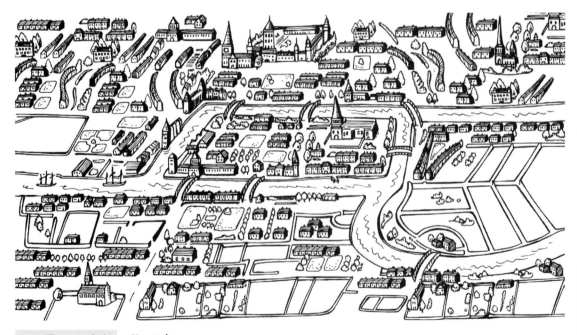

FIGURE 3.1    *Königsberg*

Can you find such a route?

You might find it helpful to make a copy of this map.

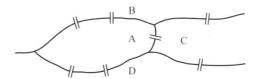

FIGURE 3.2

Does the scale of the map matter? Does it matter where you start?

If you try this puzzle, you should notice that it does not seem to have an obvious solution. Perhaps it is impossible? Or, perhaps there is a solution, but it is difficult to spot?

The puzzle of the Königsberg bridges was eventually analysed by the Swiss mathematician Leonhard Euler, who used a novel approach to demonstrate that no solution was possible. Euler's approach was based on the concept of *traversability*.

A graph is said to be *traversable* if it is possible to travel along every edge exactly once in a continuous journey, returning to your starting place.

There are four distinct pieces of land, labelled A, B, C, D in figure 3.2. These may be modelled by four vertices in a graph. The bridges may be modelled by edges connecting the vertices, as shown in figure 3.3 below.

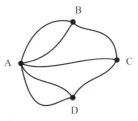

FIGURE 3.3

The problem, then, consists of trying to trace over this graph so that each edge is used exactly once.

Euler realised that the existence of a solution depends on the number of edges converging at each node; this is known as the *order* or *degree* or *valency* of that node. The node at A is of order 5, and the others are of order 3.

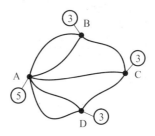

FIGURE 3.4

Every time you visit a node, two of the edges are used up: one in arriving at that node and another in leaving. When you visit A and leave again, two edges are used up. The next time you visit A and leave again, another two are used up. Then, on the third visit to A, you use the one remaining edge and hence become 'stuck' at A.

Since all four nodes have an odd order, a similar problem exists at all the nodes, and the puzzle therefore does not possess a solution.

You can immediately assess whether a given graph is traversable or not by counting the number of odd nodes (which will always be an even number). There are three possible scenarios.

No odd nodes                    The graph is fully traversable.
                                You can start anywhere and return to the start point.
                                A graph with no odd nodes is called *Eulerian*.

Two odd nodes                   The graph is semi-traversable or *semi-Eulerian*.
                                You must start at one odd node and finish at the other.

More than two odd nodes         The graph is not traversable.

EXERCISE 3A

(a) Make a sketch of each of these graphs and label the order of the nodes.
(b) For each graph, decide whether it is fully traversable, semi-traversable or not traversable.
(c) For those that are traversable or semi-traversable, show how this may be done.

1 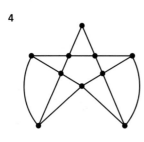 2 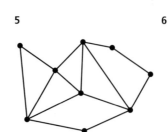 3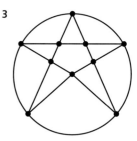

4 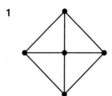 5 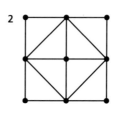 6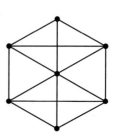

# THE ROUTE INSPECTION (CHINESE POSTMAN) PROBLEM

When heavy frost is forecast, local councils send gritting lorries out on to the roads. It is important that the lorries should travel along every road but, if possible, they should avoid using the same road twice. The lorries need to start and finish at the same place, the gritting depot. How may this be achieved?

This is an example of the route inspection problem, so named because each route needs to be inspected, or travelled along.

You can analyse a route inspection problem by drawing a network and checking it for traversability.

If there are no odd nodes the solution is easy: the network is fully traversable and it is possible to travel along each road exactly once.

If there are two odd nodes then you must convert them into even nodes by repeating some of the arcs in the network, i.e. travelling along some roads more than once. You would aim to do this in the most efficient manner possible.

If there are four odd nodes then you must join them up in pairs to convert them into even nodes. You must consider all possible pairings: there will be three combinations.

(Your A level examination will not ask you to consider more than four odd nodes because the combinations start to become less manageable.)

**EXAMPLE 3.1**

A scout group orienteering race is scheduled to take place but there has been a period of wet weather. Martin, one of the organisers, wants to walk around the course first, to check that it is safe. The checkpoints A to H are indicated in figure 3.5. Arcs between them represent the permitted footpaths and the numbers give the walking times in minutes. Martin wants to start and finish at checkpoint A.

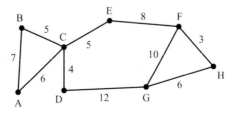

FIGURE 3.5

(a) Explain how you can tell that Martin must travel along some footpaths more than once.

(b) Find the quickest possible time for the route inspection and suggest a possible route.

*Solution*

(a) There are two odd nodes, at F and G, so the network is not traversable. Thus Martin must use some footpaths more than once.

(b) Nodes F and G must be connected in order to make them even. The direct connection, FG, could be used, adding 10 minutes. However there is a shorter (faster) option, namely to use the indirect connection FHG, adding only 9 minutes. Of course, node H then becomes order 4 rather than order 2, but this doesn't matter as it remains even. The solution is shown in figure 3.6.

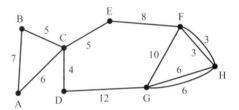

FIGURE 3.6

The minimum time is 7 + 5 + 6 + 4 + 5 + 8 + 12 + 10 + 3 + 3 + 6 + 6 = 75 minutes.

A possible route for Martin is ABCEFHFGHGDCA. (This is not unique.)

---

**EXAMPLE 3.2**

A road maintenance crew have to paint white lines up the middle of the roads in a rural area. The road network is illustrated in figure 3.7, with nodes representing the villages and arcs the connecting roads. Distances are given in kilometres, though the drawing is not to scale.

The crew must start and finish at village A.

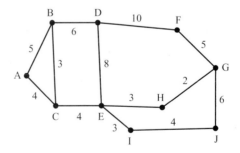

FIGURE 3.7

The supervisor says: 'The total length of all the roads is 63 km, so the crew will have to travel a total distance of 63 km to achieve their task'.

(a) Explain why the supervisor's statement is incorrect.

(b) Solve the route inspection problem, giving the shortest distance that the crew must travel in order to travel along each road at least once. Suggest a possible route to achieve this.

*Solution*
**(a)** The network is not traversable, since not all the nodes are of even order. Thus a route inspection will be longer than 63 km, the sum of the road lengths.

**(b)** There are four odd nodes, B, C, D and G, as shown in figure 3.8.

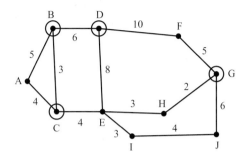

**FIGURE 3.8**

The possible pairings are BC and DG or BD and CG or BG and CD.

BC and DG      BC = 3 and DG = 13 (via E and H), total 16
BD and CG      BD = 6 and CG = 9 (via E and H), total 15
BG and CD      BG = 12 (via C, E and H) and CD = 9 (via B), total 21

So the BD and CG combination is the most efficient.

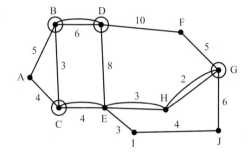

**FIGURE 3.9**

The distance the crew must travel is 63 + 6 + 4 + 3 + 2 = 78 kilometres.

A possible route is ABDBCEDFGHEHGJIECA.

**Historical note**

The route inspection problem is also called the Chinese postman problem because it was a Chinese mathematician who first described it. Route inspection, of course, is closely related to how a postman should determine the most efficient route for delivering mail.

1 The diagram shows the network of paths in a children's play area, with the lengths, in metres, of these paths.

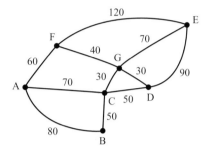

The owner wishes to inspect all of these paths. He wishes to walk the minimum distance.

(a) Using an appropriate algorithm, obtain a suitable route starting and finishing at A.

(b) Calculate the total length of this route.

[Edexcel]

2 The diagram shows a new small business park. The vertices A, B, C, D, E, F and G represent the various buildings and the arcs represent footpaths. The number on an arc gives the length, in metres, of the path.

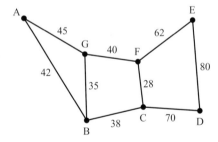

The management wishes to inspect each path to make sure it is fit for use.

Starting and finishing at A, solve the route inspection (Chinese postman) problem for the network shown in the diagram and hence determine the minimum distance that needs to be walked in carrying out this inspection. Make your method and working clear and give a possible route of minimum length.

[Edexcel]

**3** The diagram shows the network of paths in a country park. The number on each path gives its length in kilometres. The vertices A and I represent the two gates in the park and the vertices B, C, D, E, F, G and H represent places of interest.

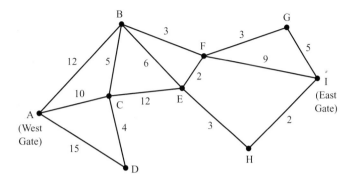

(a) Use Dijkstra's algorithm to find the shortest route from A to I. Show all necessary working in boxes at the vertices on a copy of the diagram and state your shortest route and its length.

The park warden wishes to inspect each of the paths to check for frost damage. She has to cycle along each path at least once, starting and finishing at A.

(b) (i) Use an appropriate algorithm to find which paths will be covered twice and state these paths.

(ii) Find a route of minimum length.

(iii) Find the total length of this shortest route.

[Edexcel]

**4** The diagram models an underground network of pipes that must be inspected for leaks. The nodes A, B, C, D, E, F, G and H represent entry points to the network. The number on each arc gives the length, in metres, of the corresponding pipe.

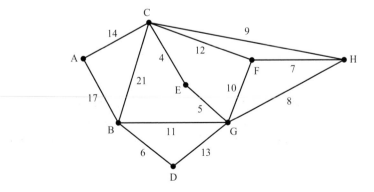

Each pipe must be traversed at least once and the length of the inspection route must be minimised.

(a)  Use the route inspection algorithm to find which paths, if any, need to be traversed twice.

It is decided to start the inspection at node C. The inspection must still traverse each pipe at least once but may finish at any node.

(b)  Explaining your reasoning briefly, determine the node at which the inspection should finish if the route is to be minimised. State the length of your route.

[Edexcel]

5  The arcs in the diagram represent roads in a town. The weight on each arc gives the time, in minutes, taken to drive along that road. The times taken to drive along AB and DE vary depending upon the time of day.

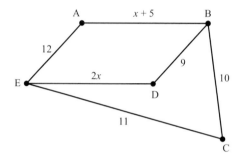

A police officer wishes to drive along each road at least once, starting and finishing at A. The journey is to be completed in the least time.

(a)  Briefly explain how you know that a route between B and E will have to be repeated.

(b)  List the possible routes between B and E. State how long each would take, in terms of $x$ where appropriate.

(c)  Find the range of values that $x$ must satisfy so that DE would be one of the repeated arcs.

Given that $x = 7$,

(d)  find the total time needed for the police officer to carry out this journey.

[Edexcel]

6 The graph is a representation of a system of roads. The length of the roads are shown in metres.

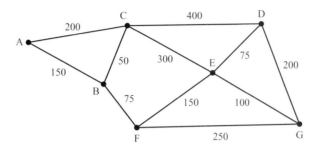

(a) List the odd vertices in the graph.

(b) Explain why the graph is not Eulerian (i.e. not traversable).

(c) By considering ways of pairing the odd vertices, find the shortest route, starting and finishing at A, and traversing each road at least once. State the length of your route.

[AEB]

7 The map shows a number of roads in a housing estate. Road intersections are labelled with capital letters and the distances in metres between intersections are shown. The total length of all the roads in the estate is 2300 m.

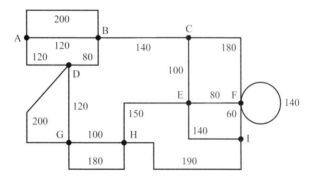

A newspaper deliverer has to walk along each road at least once, starting and ending at A. The shortest route to achieve this is required.

(a) List those intersections which are of odd order and explain their significance to the problem.

(b) By investigating all possible pairings of odd intersections, find the minimum distance which the newspaper deliverer has to walk (You are not required to apply a shortest distance algorithm to solve this. You are required to show distance computations which lead to you choosing a particular pairing of odd intersections).

(c) For each intersection other than A, give the number of times that the newspaper deliverer must pass through that intersection whilst following the shortest route.

[MEI, part]

# KEY POINTS

1  In a network, the order of a node is the number of arcs meeting at that node. Any network will always have either no odd nodes or an even number of odd nodes.

2  The route inspection (Chinese postman) problem is concerned with trying to travel along each arc of a network exactly once, if possible.

3  If there are no odd nodes then the network is traversable, and the route inspection problem has an immediate solution.

4  If there are two odd nodes then these must be joined to each other, so they both become even. This connection may be direct or it may be indirect via some intermediate node(s).

5  If there are four odd nodes then they must be joined in pairs. You must consider all possible pairings of odd nodes, for example AB and CD, AC and BD, AD and BC, and determine which one involves the least amount of extra travelling.

# Chapter four

# CRITICAL PATH ANALYSIS

When it comes to life, the critical thing is whether you take things for granted or take them with gratitude.

*G K Chesterton*

. . . . . . . . . . . . . . . . . . .

## PRECEDENCE TABLES AND ACTIVITY NETWORKS

Critical path analysis is used to understand how to manage a project containing a number of different activities. The overall aim is to produce a plan of how the activities might be scheduled, in order to complete the project in an efficient way.

Consider, for example, the steps, or activities, involved in the production of a compact disc. A simplified model of the activities might be as follows.

| Activity | | Duration (weeks) |
|---|---|---|
| A | Tape the performance | 10 |
| B | Design the cover | 9 |
| C | Book advert space in press | 3 |
| D | Convert tape to CD | 2 |
| E | Produce the cover | 4 |
| F | Packing | 1 |
| G | Send promotion copies to radio stations | 1 |
| H | Dispatch to shops | 3 |
| I | Played on radio | 2 |
| J | Place adverts in press | 1 |

How long does it take to complete the whole project?

The answer is not 10 + 9 + 3 + ... + 1 = 36 weeks, because some of the activities can take place at the same time as each other. For example, you can design the cover while the performance is being taped. Other activities, however, must occur in sequence. For example, you cannot dispatch the CD to the shops until the packing has been completed.

This new table shows the information about the activities again, along with their immediate predecessors.

| Activity | | Duration (weeks) | Immediate predecessors |
|---|---|---|---|
| A | Tape the performance | 10 | – |
| B | Design the cover | 9 | – |
| C | Book advert space in press | 3 | – |
| D | Convert tape to CD | 2 | A |
| E | Produce the cover | 4 | B |
| F | Packing | 1 | D, E |
| G | Send promotion copies to radio stations | 1 | D, E |
| H | Dispatch to shops | 3 | F |
| I | Played on radio | 2 | G |
| J | Place adverts in press | 1 | C, H, I |

This section demonstrates how to draw a network to show how the activities must be arranged. The activities will form the edges, or arcs, of the network.

Begin by marking activities A, B, C along arcs.

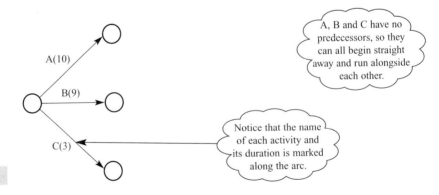

A(10)

B(9)

C(3)

A, B and C have no predecessors, so they can all begin straight away and run alongside each other.

Notice that the name of each activity and its duration is marked along the arc.

FIGURE 4.1

Activity D cannot begin until A is complete, so it must appear after A, to the right. Similarly, E cannot start until B is complete.

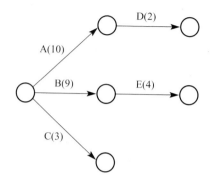

FIGURE 4.2

Now there is a problem! Activity F has both D *and* E as its immediate predecessors. You do not mark two activity Fs on the diagram. Instead you redraw the network diagram so that activities D and E converge on the same node, as shown in figure 4.3.

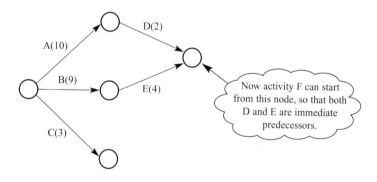

Now activity F can start from this node, so that both D and E are immediate predecessors.

FIGURE 4.3

Next, add activities F and G, both of which require D and E as their predecessors.

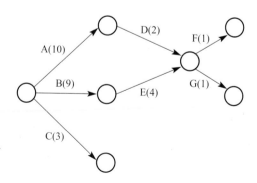

FIGURE 4.4

Now add activities H and I.

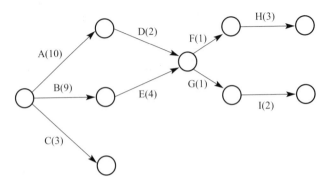

FIGURE 4.5

Finally, add activity J, which requires C, H and I as its predecessors. In order to do this, C, H and I must all converge on a single node, so it is necessary to adjust the network drawing as shown in figure 4.6.

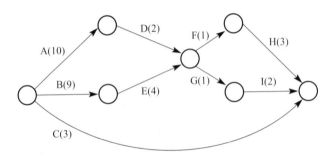

FIGURE 4.6

This allows activity J to take its place at the right-hand end, and the diagram is now complete.

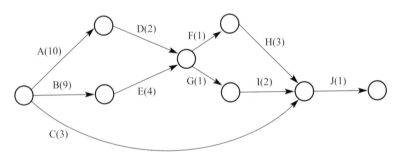

FIGURE 4.7

Remember that the activities are placed along the arcs, so this type of diagram is called an *activity-on-arc precedence diagram*. The nodes correspond to activities starting or finishing, and these are termed *events*.

Sometimes it can be helpful to refer to the events by using a numbering system, 1, 2, 3, ..., and this is normally done so that each activity carries you from a lower numbered event to a higher number one, such as is shown in figure 4.8.

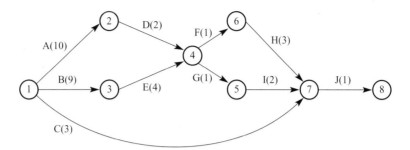

FIGURE 4.8

The network diagram shows all the information contained in the precedence table. This diagram can be analysed to find the shortest duration for the project, and this will be done shortly. Before doing so, however, the following points should be noted carefully.

- The diagram has a unique start event, 1, and a unique finish event, 8.

- Activities, with their durations, are represented along the arcs.

- It is possible for several activities to diverge from the same event, for example, A, B, C diverge from event 1.

- It is possible for several activities to converge on the same event, for example, D and E converge on event 4.

You should not allow the same pair of activities to diverge from one node and converge on another, however. If the logic of the precedence table seems to be requiring this, then it is necessary to introduce a dummy variable, as discussed in the next section. Dummies are also required when the same immediate predecessor activity occurs in two different contexts in the precedence table.

## DUMMY ACTIVITIES

Suppose you are constructing a network diagram for a precedence table which contains the following components.

| Activity | Immediate predecessors |
|:---:|:---:|
| A | – |
| B | – |
| C | A |
| D | A, B |
| etc. | etc. |

Look carefully at the immediate predecessors column and you will notice an obvious difficulty, namely that activity A occurs in two different contexts: once on its own and again in combination with B. This is an immediate indication that a dummy activity will be required.

A *dummy activity* has *zero duration*. Dummies are used, when necessary, in order to maintain the logic of the precedence table.

In the case of the table on page 79, you need to have a node fed by activity A only and another fed by activities A and B together. This may be achieved as shown in figure 4.9.

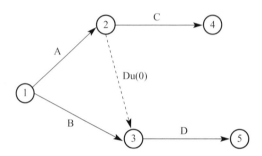

FIGURE 4.9

Activity D originates from node 3, which requires that B and the dummy are both completed first. Since the dummy requires A to be completed first (seen at node 2), then this forces A to be a predecessor for D, so the required logic is maintained in the diagram.

You should always scan the precedence table to check for dummies before attempting to draw the network diagram.

### EXAMPLE 4.1

The tasks involved in decorating a room are given in the table.

| Activity | | Immediate predecessors |
|---|---|---|
| A | Strip old paper | – |
| B | Rub down wooden surfaces | – |
| C | Paint ceiling | A |
| D | Apply undercoat | A, B |
| E | Apply gloss paint | D |
| F | Paper walls | C, E |

Draw an activity-on-arc network to illustrate this information.

*Solution*    Looking at the predecessors, you can see that A arises in two different ways: once on its own and once in conjunction with B. No other activities do this, so only one dummy is required.

The complete network diagram is shown in figure 4.10.

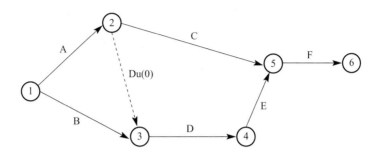

**FIGURE 4.10**

**Note**    As mentioned earlier, you might also need to use a dummy occasionally simply to preserve the unique labelling of event nodes. You should never have two activities sharing the same start and finish nodes.

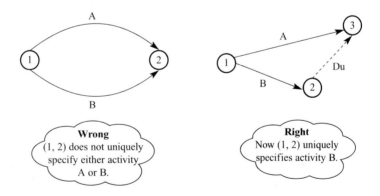

**FIGURE 4.11**

EXERCISE 4A    **1** The diagram shows an activity-on-arc precedence diagram.

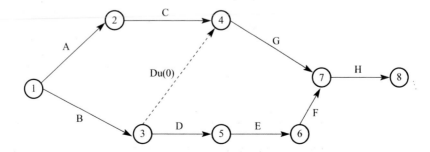

Copy the precedence table and fill in the missing information.

| Activity | Immediate predecessors |
|----------|------------------------|
| A | – |
| B | – |
| C | A |
| D | |
| E | |
| F | |
| G | |
| H | |

2  The diagram shows an activity-on-arc precedence diagram.

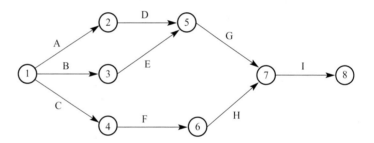

Copy the precedence table and fill in the missing information.

| Activity | Immediate predecessors |
|----------|------------------------|
| A | – |
| B | – |
| C | – |
| D | A |
| E | |
| F | |
| G | |
| H | |
| I | |

3 The table below shows some activities, together with their durations and immediate predecessors, required to complete a small project.

| Activity | Duration | Immediate predecessors |
|----------|----------|------------------------|
| A | 4 | – |
| B | 2 | – |
| C | 3 | A |
| D | 6 | B |
| E | 1 | D |
| F | 5 | C, E |
| G | 1 | C, E |
| H | 3 | G |

(a) Explain why no dummy activities will be needed in the activity-on-arc network diagram, even though activities C and E appear more than once in the immediate predecessors column.

(b) Construct the activity-on-arc diagram.

4 The table below shows some activities, together with their durations and immediate predecessors, required to complete a small project.

| Activity | Duration | Immediate predecessors |
|----------|----------|------------------------|
| A | 2 | – |
| B | 4 | A |
| C | 6 | A |
| D | 3 | A |
| E | 6 | D |
| F | 1 | B |
| G | 1 | C |
| H | 1 | F, G |
| I | 6 | E, H |
| J | 5 | E |

(a) Explain how the table shows you that exactly one dummy activity will be needed in order to draw the activity-on-arc network diagram.

(b) Construct the activity-on-arc diagram.

5 The table below shows some activities, together with their durations and immediate predecessors, required to complete a project.

| Activity | Duration | Immediate predecessors |
|----------|----------|------------------------|
| A | 4 | – |
| B | 2 | A |
| C | 2 | A |
| D | 1 | B |
| E | 3 | D |
| F | 5 | C |
| G | 2 | E, F |
| H | 9 | C |
| I | 4 | G, H |

Construct an activity-on-arc diagram for the project.

# FINDING THE CRITICAL PATH

Consider again the CD project discussed earlier in this chapter. The activity-on-arc network diagram looked like this.

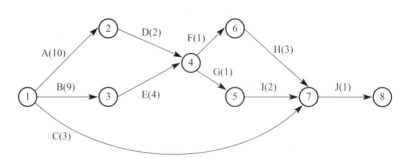

FIGURE 4.12

You can use the diagram to determine how early, or late, the activities might be scheduled to take place. In order to do this, you need to add some boxes at the event nodes, as shown in figure 4.13.

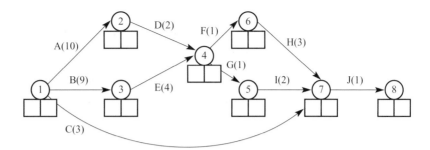

FIGURE 4.13

Now assume the project starts at time zero. Use the left-hand box at each event node to record the *early time*, i.e. the earliest time you could be at a node having completed all the activities feeding into it. You can fill in the early times at nodes 1, 2 and 3 immediately, as shown in figure 4.14.

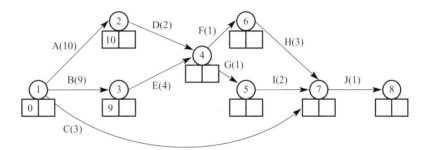

FIGURE 4.14

Next consider node 4. The route using activity D suggests an early time of $10 + 2 = 12$, whereas the value for the route using E will be $9 + 4 = 13$. Since you wish to arrive at node 4 with all the preceding activities completed, you must take the higher of these two values, i.e. 13, and record that as the early time for node 4, as shown in figure 4.15.

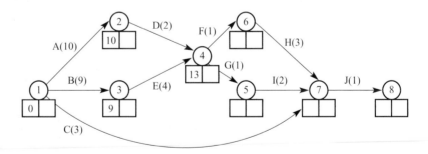

FIGURE 4.15

You continue in a similar way to complete the *forward pass*. The result is shown in figure 4.16.

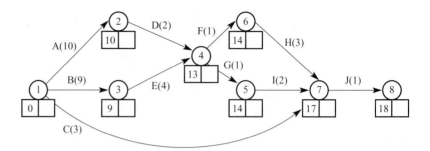

FIGURE 4.16

The forward pass through the diagram establishes the earliest times by which the activities feeding each node may be completed. The next step is to carry out a *backward pass*. You begin by writing the value from the left-hand box at the last node, in the right-hand box at that node. You then start tracing back through the diagram, as shown in figure 4.17.

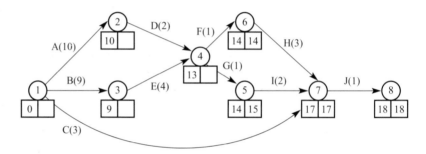

FIGURE 4.17

Now, consider carefully what happens at node 4. The two options are 14 − 1 = 13 and 15 − 1 = 14. Remember that these late times tell you how late you may depart from node 4 in order to reach nodes 5 and 6 on time when moving forwards through the diagram. Thus you must take the lower of these two values, i.e. 13, otherwise you would be late getting to node 6.

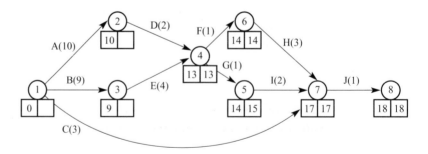

FIGURE 4.18

You continue in a similar way to complete the diagram. It is shown in figure 4.19.

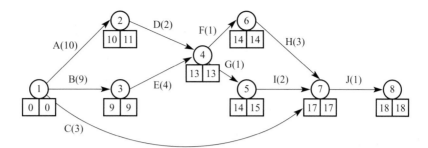

FIGURE 4.19

If you look at the diagram carefully, you will see that some of the activities have their start and finish times precisely specified. For example, activity H must start at time 14 and finish at time 17. This activity is *critical*.

On the other hand, some activities have more flexibility over their timings. For example, activity D could start as early as time 10 and must finish by time 13 but, since it only lasts for duration 2, there is some spare time, or *float*, associated with this activity.

You are now in a position to look for the *critical path*, i.e. the set of all the critical activities. This is normally done by starting at the finish node, node 8, and tracing back though the diagram. The critical nodes are identified by their early and late times being identical, and the critical activities are identified by being just the right length to completely fill the time between two critical nodes. So J is critical because it is of duration 1, and 18 – 17 = 1 also. Then use H, because 17 – 14 = 3 matches the duration of H, which is also 3. Continuing in this way results in the diagram shown in figure 4.20.

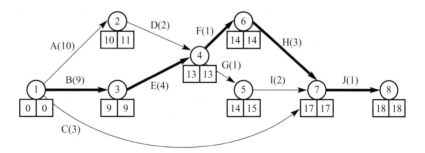

FIGURE 4.20

The critical activities are B, E, F, H and J. They are called critical because a delay with any of them will cause the whole project to be delayed.

The critical path is BEFHJ. The activities with float are A, C, D, G, I.

# FLOAT

If you look carefully at the example on p.87, you may notice that all of the activities, except the critical ones, have a certain amount of flexibility about when they could take place.

Activity C, for example, could start at time 0 and be finished by time 3, since its duration is only 3 units of time (weeks). On the other hand, it could start as late as time 14, and still be completed by time 17.

This flexibility is known as *the total float*, and may be calculated as follows.

$$\text{Total float} = \text{Late time at finish event} - \text{early time at start event} - \text{duration of activity}$$

For activity C, this would give a total float of $17 - 0 - 3 = 14$.

Similarly, for activity D, the total float is $13 - 10 - 2 = 1$.

---

### EXAMPLE 4.2

The table shows the durations and precedences for the seven activities in a project.

| Activity | Duration (days) | Immediate predecessors |
|----------|-----------------|------------------------|
| A | 2 | – |
| B | 7 | – |
| C | 4 | A |
| D | 1 | B |
| E | 3 | B, C |
| F | 1 | D |
| G | 2 | E, F |

(a) Explain how the table indicates that you will need one dummy activity in the activity-on-arc diagram.

(b) Construct this diagram.

(c) Perform forward and backward passes, and hence identify the critical activities. State the minimum completion time for the project.

(d) It is subsequently discovered that activity D will require 2 days, not 1. Explain carefully the effect that this will have on
   (i) the minimum completion time for the project
   (ii) the scheduling of the activities in the project.

*Solution*   (a)   Looking at the various predecessors, you can see that activity B occurs on its own in one row and in conjunction with activity C in another. Thus a dummy will be needed in connection with activity B.

(b)–(c)   The activity-on-arc diagram after the forward and backward passes have been performed is shown in figure 4.21.

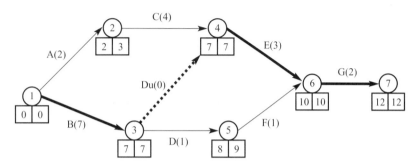

**FIGURE 4.21**

The critical activities are B, E and G.

The minimum completion time is 12 days.

> Notice that even though the dummy is on the critical path, you do not include it in the final list of critical activities, since it does not correspond to a real activity.

(d)   (i)   Since activity D has an existing float of 1 it is possible to absorb the extra day so that the minimum completion time does not change.

(ii)   Activities D and F have now lost their float, so activity D must start at time 7 and activity F at time 9 in order to complete the project on time.

---

EXERCISE 4B   **1**   In parts **(a)** to **(d)** you are given an activity-on-arc precedence diagram for a set of activities. Copy the diagram and perform forward and backward passes to obtain the early and late times for each event. Hence find the minimum duration for the entire set of activities and state the critical activities.

**(a)**

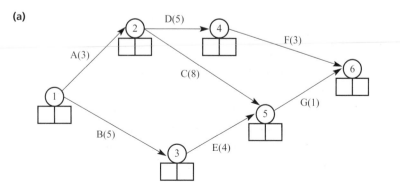

**(b)**

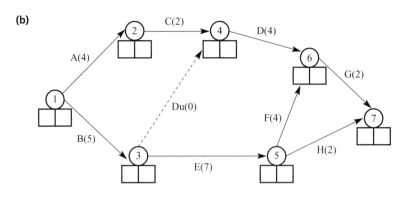

**(c)**

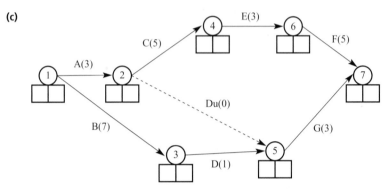

**(d)**

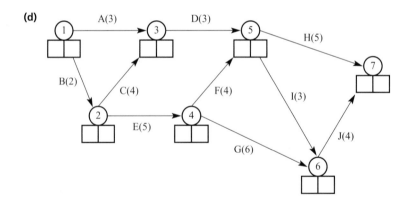

2 Claire wants to prepare and eat her breakfast in the minimum time.
The activities involved, their immediate predecessors and their durations are
shown in the table.

| Activity | | Immediate predecessors | Duration (mins) |
|---|---|---|---|
| F | Fill kettle | – | 0.5 |
| I | Put instant coffee in cup | – | 0.5 |
| W | Boil water | F | 10 |
| G | Grill toast | – | 7 |
| D | Dish out cereal | – | 0.5 |
| O | Fetch and open milk | – | 0.5 |
| M | Make coffee | I, W | 0.5 |
| B | Butter toast | G | 0.5 |
| E | Eat cereal and milk | D, O | 3 |
| T | Eat toast | E, B | 5 |
| C | Drink coffee | M, T | 3 |

(a) Draw an activity-on-arc network for these activities. Do not take account of the fact that Claire can do only one thing at a time.

(b) Show on your network the earliest time and the latest time for each event.

(c) Give the critical activities and the minimum time needed for Claire to complete her breakfast, again taking no account of the fact that she can do only one thing at a time.

[MEI, *part*]

3 The table shows the precedences for the four tasks of a project. The duration of each task is also shown.

| Task | Immediate predecessor(s) | Duration (days) |
|---|---|---|
| A | – | 2 |
| B | – | 1 |
| C | A | 1 |
| D | A, B | 3 |

(a) Draw an activity-on-arc network to represent this information.

(b) Find the early and late event times.

(c) Give the total float for each activity.

[MEI]

4  The precedences and durations for the activities of a project are shown in the table.

| Activity | Immediate predecessors | Duration |
|----------|------------------------|----------|
| A | – | 2 |
| B | – | 3 |
| C | A, B | 4 |
| D | B | 2 |
| E | C | 7 |
| F | C, D | 3 |
| G | C, D | 5 |
| H | F, G | 2 |

(a)  Draw an activity-on-arc network for the project.

(b)  Find the critical activities.

[MEI]

# CASCADE CHARTS

Cascade charts are sometimes called Gantt charts.

**Historical note**

They were developed by the American engineer Henry Laurence Gantt in the 1910s. By the 1920s they were being used worldwide in the management of large projects, and featured in the planning for the construction of the Hoover Dam in 1931.

A cascade chart is a way of displaying the timings for the different activities. The critical activities are marked in as firm timings, since they have no float. The non-critical activities may then be marked in, using outline boxes, to show how they could be scheduled at their earliest possible times. Grey boxes are added on to indicate float where appropriate. To illustrate this, look again at the diagram from Example 4.2 on page 89.

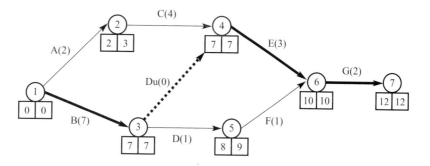

FIGURE 4.23

To make the cascade chart, you begin by drawing a time line, long enough to last the length of the whole project, in this case, 12 days. Then make a grid underneath and place the critical activities across the top of the grid, in their correct sequence, as shown in figure 4.24.

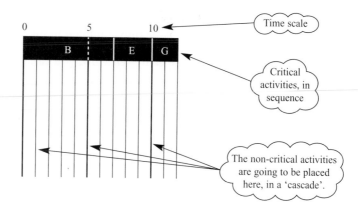

FIGURE 4.24

Activity A could start as early as time 0, and is then followed by activity C.
A and C must be completed by time 7.

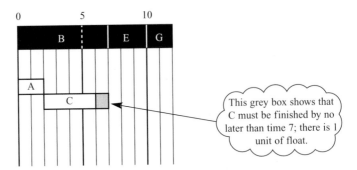

FIGURE 4.25

Finally, D and F are placed in the cascade.

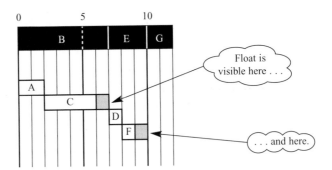

FIGURE 4.26

# SCHEDULING

In some projects the resources available for each activity may be in limited supply.
For example, there may be only a limited number of workers available.

By reading the cascade chart vertically, you can see which activities are scheduled to
be happening at the same time. If there are insufficient resources to manage this,
then one or more of the activities must be rescheduled to a later time, possibly
causing the minimum completion time to increase.

**EXAMPLE 4.3**

The tasks involved in erecting a garden shed are given in the table.

| Task | | Time (hours) | Immediate predecessors |
|---|---|---|---|
| A | Clear the area | 1 | – |
| B | Unpack shed kit | 0.5 | – |
| C | Prepare foundations | 1 | A |
| D | Erect walls | 1 | A, B, C |
| E | Attach roof | 0.5 | D |
| F | Fit door | 0.5 | D |
| G | Attach window kit | 1 | D |
| H | Attach roofing felt | 1 | E |
| I | Fit handles and locks | 1 | F |

(a) Draw an activity-on-arc diagram.

(b) Perform a forward pass and a backward pass through your diagram, to find the early and late times for each event.

(c) Find the minimum completion time and the corresponding critical activities.

(d) Draw a cascade chart for the project, assuming that each task begins as early as possible.

In fact, each task requires one person, and there are only two people available.

(e) Using your cascade chart, explain why it is not possible to complete the project in the minimum time you found in part (c).

(f) By rescheduling one or more tasks, find the new minimum completion time.

*Solution*    (a)–(b) The activity-on-arc diagram after the forward and backward passes have been performed is shown in figure 4.27.

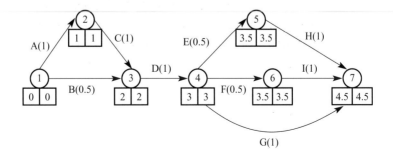

**FIGURE 4.27**

(c) The minimum completion time is 4.5 hours.
   The critical activities are A, C, D, E, F, H and I.

(d) The cascade chart is shown in figure 4.28.

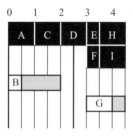

FIGURE 4.28

(e) The project cannot be completed in 4.5 hours with only two people available, since activity G will clash with some or all of activities E, F, H and I.

(f) By rescheduling activities F, H and I to run half an hour later than their earliest start times this clash is resolved. The minimum completion time now becomes 5 hours.

EXERCISE 4C   **1** The table gives information about a construction project.

| Activity | Duration (days) | Immediate predecessors |
|----------|-----------------|------------------------|
| A | 10 | – |
| B | 3 | – |
| C | 5 | B |
| D | 3 | A, C |
| E | 4 | B |
| F | 7 | D |
| G | 2 | C, E |

(a) Copy and complete the precedence diagram for the project.

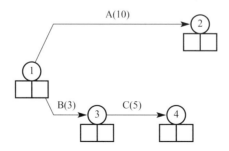

(b) Perform a forward pass and a backward pass on your precedence network to determine the earliest and latest event times.

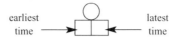

earliest time    latest time

(c) State the minimum time for completion and the critical activities.

(d) Use an appropriate method to produce an ordering of the activities, and hence draw a cascade chart for the project.

2 The tasks involved in decorating a room are given in the table.

| Task | | Immediate predecessors |
|------|--|------------------------|
| A | Strip old paper | – |
| B | Rub down wooden surfaces | – |
| C | Paint ceiling | A |
| D | Apply undercoat | A, B |
| E | Apply gloss paint | D |
| F | Paper walls | C, E |

(a) Draw an activity-on-arc network to illustrate this information.

The duration of each task is shown in table below.

| Task | A | B | C | D | E | F |
|------|---|---|---|---|---|---|
| Duration (days) | 1 | 0.25 | 0.75 | 1 | 1 | 1 |

(b) Complete forward and backward passes to find the earliest and latest event times. Give the critical activities and the minimum duration of the project.

(c) Each task requires one person. Fred is decorating the room on his own. How long will it take him?

(d) Fred asks Alice to help him. Show that together they could decorate three rooms within eight days.

[MEI, part]

3 The activity network shows the durations (in days) of the nine activities of a project, and their precedences.

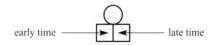

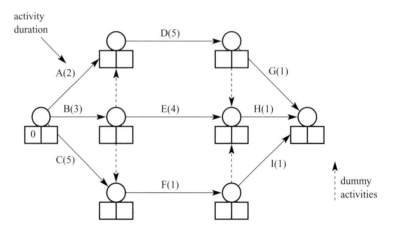

(a) Produce a table showing, for each activity, the *immediate* predecessors.

(b) Perform a forward pass and a backward pass on the activity network to find the earliest event times and latest event times.

List the critical activities and give the time for completion of the project.

(c) Produce a cascade chart, assuming that all the activities are scheduled to start as early as possible.

The activities require resources (people) as indicated in the table.

| Activity | A | B | C | D | E | F | G | H | I |
|---|---|---|---|---|---|---|---|---|---|
| Resources required (people) | 1 | 1 | 2 | 1 | 4 | 1 | 1 | 1 | 1 |

(d) If only six people are available, find the shortest possible time in which the project can be completed. State which activities need to be delayed in order to achieve this.

[MEI, *adapted*]

EXERCISE 4D EXAMINATION-STYLE QUESTIONS

**1** The activity-on-arc diagram gives the durations, in days, for a small project.

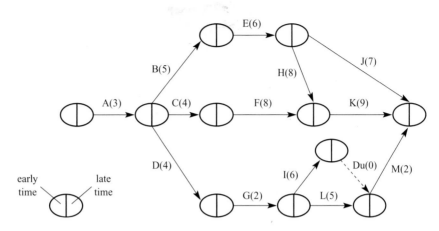

(a) Copy and complete the precedence table below.

| Activity | Duration (days) | Immediate predecessors |
|----------|-----------------|------------------------|
| A | 3 | – |
| B | 5 | A |
| C | 4 | |
| D | 4 | |
| E | 6 | |
| F | 8 | |
| G | 2 | |
| H | 8 | |
| I | 6 | |
| J | 7 | |
| K | 9 | |
| L | 5 | |
| M | 2 | |

(b) Perform a forward and a backward pass to determine the early and late times for each event.

(c) Determine the critical activities and the minimum time for completion of the project.

(d) Explain briefly the purpose of the dummy activity between activities I and M.

(e) As a result of a breakdown of a piece of equipment, activity F is now going to take 16 days instead of 8. Explain the effect this will have on the minimum time to complete the project.

2 A customer at a roadside restaurant orders a meal consisting of a beefburger with cheese filling, chips and a side salad, followed by apple pie. The activities involved in preparing, serving and eating the meal, their timings and precedences, are given in the table.

| Activity | | Immediate predecessors | Time (minutes) |
|---|---|---|---|
| A | Cook chips | – | 5 |
| B | Toast bap | – | 2 |
| C | Prepare cheese filling | – | 2 |
| D | Cook meat | – | 4 |
| E | Make up beefburger | B, C, D | 1 |
| F | Prepare salad | – | 3 |
| G | Serve main course | A, E, F | 0.5 |
| H | Eat main course | G | 15 |
| I | Heat apple pie | – | 5 |
| J | Serve apple pie | H, I | 0.5 |
| K | Eat apple pie | J | 9 |

(a) Draw an activity-on-arc network to represent this information.

(b) Find the early time and the late time for each event on your network, labelling them clearly on your diagram.

(c) The customer arrives at 1215 and is to finish the meal by 1245. Complete the table to schedule the activities as late as possible.

| Activity | | Activity start time | Activity end time |
|---|---|---|---|
| A | Cook chips | | |
| B | Toast bap | | |
| C | Prepare cheese filling | | |
| D | Cook meat | | |
| E | Make up beefburger | | |
| F | Prepare salad | | |
| G | Serve main course | | |
| H | Eat main course | | |
| I | Heat apple pie | | |
| J | Serve apple pie | | |
| K | Eat apple pie | | |

[MEI, *part*]

**3** The diagram below shows a precedence diagram. Activity durations are in days, and are shown in brackets against the arc representing the activity. Activity X connects event 6 to event 8.

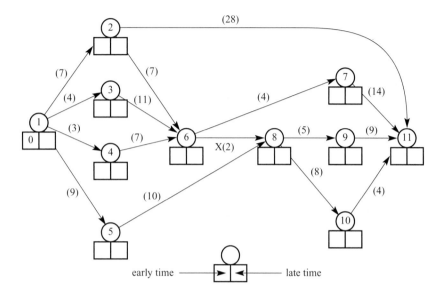

early time ————▷|◁———— late time

(a) Perform a forward pass on this network.

Give the earliest time for event number 6 and the earliest time for event number 8.

(b) Perform a backward pass on the network.

Give the latest time for event number 8 and the latest time for event number 6.

(c) The network opposite is part of a larger network. It shows all of the activities which are connected to activity X, *and only those activities*, together with some earliest and latest times.

Say which of the following it is possible to compute from the information given on this network. In each case do the computation if it is possible, and say why it is not possible if not.

(i)   The earliest time for event 52.
(ii)  The earliest time for event 58.
(iii) The latest time for event 50.
(iv) The latest time for event 35.

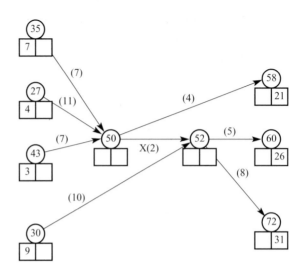

[MEI, *part*]

4  The precedence table for activities involved in a small project is shown below.

| Activity | Preceding activities |
|:---:|:---:|
| A | – |
| B | – |
| C | – |
| D | B |
| E | A |
| F | A |
| G | B |
| H | C, D |
| I | E |
| J | E |
| K | F, G, I |
| L | H, J, K |

Draw an activity network, using activity on edge and without using dummies, to model this project.

[Edexcel]

5 The diagram shows the activity network used to model a small building project. The activities are represented by the edges and the number in brackets on each edge represents the time, in hours, taken to complete that activity.

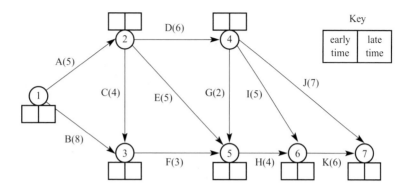

(a) Copy the diagram. Calculate the early time and the late time for each event, labelling them clearly on your diagram.

(b) Hence determine the critical activities and the length of the critical path.

Each activity requires one worker. The project is to be completed in the minimum time.

(c) Schedule the activities for the minimum number of workers and show them in a diagram. Ensure that you make clear the order in which each worker undertakes his activities.

[Edexcel]

6 A project is modelled by the activity network shown below. The activities are represented by the edges. The number in brackets on each edge gives the time, in days, to complete the activity.

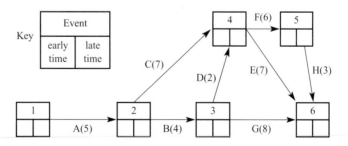

(a) Make a copy of the network diagram. Calculate the early time and the late time for each event, and write these in the boxes on your diagram.

(b) Hence determine the critical activities and the length of the critical path.

(c) Obtain the total float for each of the non-critical activities.

(d) Draw a cascade (Gantt) chart showing the information obtained in parts (b) and (c).

Each activity requires one worker. Only two workers are available.

**(e)** Make a grid and draw up a schedule to find the minimum time in which two workers can complete the project.

[Edexcel]

**7** A building project is modelled by the activity network shown below. The activities are represented by the arcs. The number in brackets on each arc gives the time, in hours, taken to complete the activity. The left box entry at each vertex is the earliest event time and the right box entry is the latest event time.

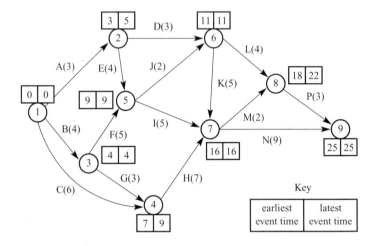

**(a)** Determine the critical activities and state the length of the critical path.

**(b)** State the total float for each non-critical activity.

**(c)** Draw a cascade (Gantt) chart for the project.

Given that each activity requires one worker,

**(d)** draw up a schedule to determine the minimum number of workers required to complete the project in the critical time. State the minimum number of workers.

[Edexcel]

**8** The precedence table for activities involved in manufacturing a toy is shown below.

| Activity | Preceding activity |
|----------|--------------------|
| A | – |
| B | – |
| C | – |
| D | A |
| E | A |
| F | B |
| G | B |
| H | C, D, E, F |
| I | E |
| J | E |
| K | I |
| L | I |
| M | G, H, K |

**(a)** Draw an activity network, using activity on arc, and exactly one dummy, to model the manufacturing process.

**(b)** Explain briefly why it is necessary to use a dummy in this case.

[Edexcel]

**9** A project is modelled by the activity network shown below. The activities are represented by the arcs. One worker is required for each activity. The number in brackets on each arc gives the time, in hours, to complete the activity. The earliest event time and the latest event time are given by the numbers in the left box and right box respectively.

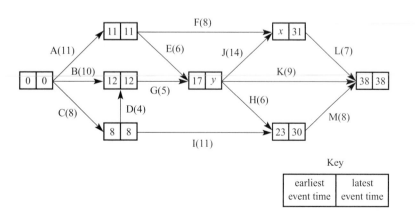

Key

| earliest event time | latest event time |
|---------------------|-------------------|

(a) State the value of $x$ and the value of $y$.

(b) List the critical activities.

(c) Explain why at least three workers will be needed to complete this project in 38 hours.

(d) Schedule the activities so that the project is completed in 38 hours using just three workers. You must make clear the start time and finish time of each activity.

[Edexcel]

10 The table shows activities involved in making a Greek salad, their precedences and their durations.

| Activity | | Immediate predecessor(s) | Duration (seconds) |
|---|---|---|---|
| A | Wash tomato | – | 15 |
| B | Slice tomato | A | 30 |
| C | Peel cucumber | – | 30 |
| D | Slice cucumber | C | 30 |
| E | Peel onion | – | 30 |
| F | Slice onion | E | 30 |
| G | Slice feta cheese | – | 15 |
| H | Prepare herbs | – | 45 |
| I | Coat feta cheese with herbs | G, H | 15 |
| J | Collect ingredients in bowl | B, D, F, I | 15 |
| K | Add olives and dressing | J | 15 |

(a) Draw an activity network for preparing the salad.

(b) Perform a forward pass and a backward pass to determine early and late event times. Give the critical activities and the minimum duration.

Several friends share the making of a Greek salad, but there is only one sharp knife. A sharp knife is needed for activities B, D, F and G.

(c) Draw a cascade chart assuming that every activity starts at its earliest start time, subject to the condition that activities B, D, F and G may not overlap. Give the total time needed to make the salad.

(d) If each activity requires one person, how many people are needed to implement the solution given by your cascade chart in part (c).

(e) Find the minimum time needed to prepare the salad if there is only one sharp knife and there are only two friends.

[MEI]

# KEY POINTS

1 A precedence table shows the durations of the activities in a project, along with the activities that must be completed in order to start them (immediate predecessors).

2 The activities are marked along the arcs of a network. The nodes are known as events.

3 Dummy activities have zero duration. They are introduced when the same activity appears in two or more different contexts in the precedence table.

4 Dummies are also used to prevent the same pair of activities from sharing the same start and finish event nodes.

5 Precedence diagrams are scanned forwards to obtain early times and backwards to obtain late times. The diagram can then be used to determine the minimum completion time for the project and whether some of the activities might have some float.

6 The total float of an activity is

   latest finish time – earliest start time – duration of activity.

7 Activities with zero float are called critical activities and the full set of these forms the critical path.

8 The scheduling of a project may be illustrated with a cascade (Gantt) chart in which the critical activities are placed along the top and the activities with float are placed in a cascade underneath.

# Chapter five

# LINEAR PROGRAMMING

Divide each difficulty into as many parts as is feasible and necessary to resolve it.

*Rene Descartes*

## INTRODUCING LINEAR PROGRAMMING

Problems in mathematics are often concerned with finding the best solution subject to certain restrictions, or constraints, that must be satisfied.

For example, suppose that Kirsty is considering buying some CDs at £10 each, and some greetings cards, at £2 each, but she only has £50 available to spend. If you use $c$ to represent the number of CDs she buys and $g$ the number of greetings cards, then the cash limit of £50 may be written as a simple inequality:

$$10c + 2g \leqslant 50.$$

This is a *linear inequality* in $c$ and $g$. If you are aiming to solve a problem in which all the constraints are linear, the resulting methodology is known as *linear programming* (LP). Two-dimensional problems may be solved by a combined graphical and algebraic method. A more general method, if somewhat fiddly, is the iterative simplex method. Although this method may also be used for two-dimensional problems, it really comes into its own when three or more dimensions are involved.

**Historical note**    Linear programming was developed during the Second World War (1939–1945) to solve problems about supply and demand of resources.

### EXAMPLE 5.1

Kirsty is considering buying some CDs, at £10 each, and some greetings cards, at £2 each, but she only has £50 available to spend. Her best friends, who are twins, have a birthday next week, so she must buy at least two CDs and at least two greetings cards.

(a) Write down five inequalities that act as constraints.

(b) Draw a graph to illustrate the possible solutions to this problem.

*Solution*

(a) Suppose she buys $c$ CDs and $g$ greetings cards.

The spending constraint, as discussed on p.108, may be written as:

$$10c + 2g \leqslant 50.$$

The birthday condition gives two further constraints:

$$2 \leqslant c$$
$$2 \leqslant g.$$

Finally, she cannot buy a negative number of CDs or greeting cards, so there are two 'non-negative' constraints:

$$0 \leqslant c$$
$$0 \leqslant g.$$

**Note**

In this particular problem, the non-negative constraints do not add any further restrictions beyond those contained in the birthday condition. This is not always the case, however, and you should always remember to include them for the sake of completeness.

(b) The initial constraint, $10c + 2g \leqslant 50$, will clearly generate a corresponding linear graph $10c + 2g = 50$ of negative gradient. The easiest way of graphing this line is to identify the points where it will cross the horizontal and vertical axes. When $g = 0$, $10c = 50$ so $c = 5$, and when $c = 0$, $2g = 50$ so $g = 25$. Thus the intercepts on the axes will be at $(5, 0)$ and $(0, 25)$.

Figure 5.1 shows the various constraints plotted on a graph. So that you can see the points you want clearly, you shade the regions you do *not* want. Since $10c + 2g$ must be *less than or equal to* 50, you shade the region *above* this line. Similarly, you shade the regions to the left of $c = 2$, and below $g = 2$. The region left unshaded satisfies *all* of the constraints and is known as the *feasible region*.

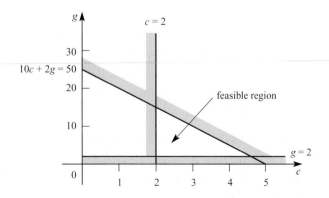

**FIGURE 5.1**

Most linear programming questions then go on to ask a question about maximising or minimising some quantity, for example cost or profit, by searching within the feasible region. Before moving on to this idea, Exercise 5A gives practice at formulating the inequalities and graphing them.

EXERCISE 5A

1 On a sheet of graph or squared paper illustrate the feasible region for the following set of constraints.

$$2x + 5y \leqslant 50$$
$$x \geqslant 5$$
$$y \geqslant 5$$

2 On a sheet of graph or squared paper illustrate the feasible region for the following set of constraints.

$$4x + 3y \leqslant 60$$
$$x \geqslant 5$$
$$x \leqslant 10$$
$$y \geqslant 8$$

3 At a plant stall at the local school fair, tomato plants and cucumber plants are on sale. The tomato plants cost 25 pence each, while the cucumber plants are 40 pence. Maria wishes to buy some of these plants. She wants to buy at least two of each kind of plant. Also, she has £10 in her purse, but wants to save at least half of this to spend on another stall.

Using $x$ as the number of tomato plants she buys and $y$ as the number of cucumber plants, write down five inequalities, including two non-negative ones. Then illustrate the feasible region on a graph.

4 A gardener decides to plant a mixture of daffodil bulbs and tulip bulbs in his flowerbed. The flowerbed cannot take more than 30 bulbs and the gardener wants to have at least 5 of each type.

Let $x$ denote the number of daffodil bulbs used and $y$ the number of tulip bulbs. Write down the constraints for this problem and then illustrate the feasible region on graph paper.

5 A teacher is making some posters to advertise the school fair. She is making two sizes, A4 and A3. She has enough materials to make at most 20 posters. The A4 posters take 5 minutes each to make, while the A3 posters take 10 minutes each, and she has two and a half hours available to make them all.

Let $x$ denote the number of A4 posters she makes and $y$ the number of A3 posters. Write down the constraints for this problem and then illustrate the feasible region on graph paper.

## GRAPHICAL SOLUTION OF TWO-VARIABLE PROBLEMS

The section looks at a full solution, using a graphical approach, to a typical two-variable problem. In solving such problems the aim is to maximise or minimise some quantity subject to a set of constraints. The method is to formulate the problem as a set of inequalities and graph the feasible region. Then you construct a function, known as the *objective function*, and explore its behaviour at different places within the feasible region.

There are two methods, the ruler method or the vertex method, both of which yield the same result.

### EXAMPLE 5.2

Suzy goes to a chocolate shop to buy some hand-made chocolates. She only likes two types: the caramels, costing 20 pence each, and the truffles, costing 25 pence. She can afford to spend up to £6 altogether. She wants to buy at least four of each type and she wants to purchase as many chocolates as possible.

Write a set of inequalities to formulate this information as a linear programming problem. Solve the problem using a graphical method.

*Solution*

Suppose Suzy buys $x$ caramels and $y$ truffles. Then the total number of chocolates is

$$x + y.$$

This is the objective function for the problem, and needs to be maximised since Suzy wants to buy as many chocolates as possible.

Thus the problem may be stated as:

Maximise $x + y$ subject to the constraints

$$20x + 25y \leqslant 600$$
$$x \geqslant 4$$
$$y \geqslant 4$$

and, of course, the non-negative conditions $x \geqslant 0$ and $y \geqslant 0$.

The graph of the feasible region in shown in figure 5.2.

You now need to maximise $x + y$ within the feasible region.

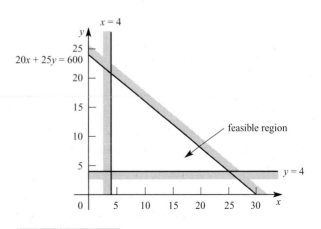

FIGURE 5.2

### Method 1: The ruler method

To maximise $x + y$, you simply consider equations of the form $x + y = c$, for example $x + y = 5$, $x + y = 10$, and so on. These may be overlaid on the graph, as shown in figure 5.3, to show a family of straight-line graphs.

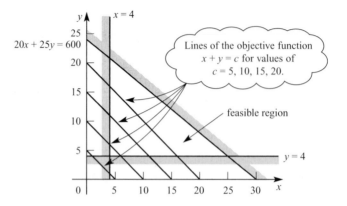

FIGURE 5.3

Now move a ruler through the feasible region, keeping its edge parallel to this family of straight lines. (You can use a ruler and set square combination for greater accuracy.) You continue moving the ruler up until it is about to exit the feasible region, then stop, and draw the solution line. The point at which this line cuts the feasible region gives the solution point, as shown in figure 5.4.

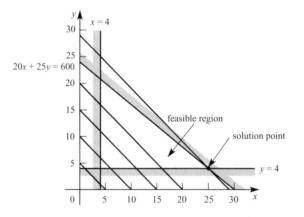

FIGURE 5.4

From the graph you can see that the solution point is at $(25, 4)$, so Suzy buys 29 chocolates in all, 25 caramels and 4 truffles.

### Method 2: The vertex method

As an alternative to the ruler method, you can instead rely on the principle that the solution line must intersect the feasible region in at least one of its vertices. So, you can just check the value of the objective function at each vertex.

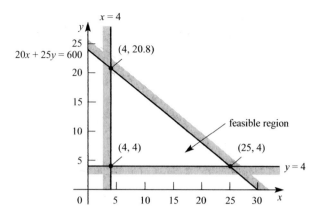

FIGURE 5.5

You tabulate the three sets of coordinates as shown here.

| Point | Value of objective function, $x + y$ |
| --- | --- |
| (4, 20.8) | 24.8 |
| (25, 4) | 29 |
| (4, 4) | 8 |

From the table you can see that the solution point is at (25, 4), so Suzy buys 29 chocolates in all, 25 caramels and 4 truffles.

**Note**

You may not be entirely happy using values like 20.8 and 24.8 since it is unlikely that the chocolate shop will want to sell 0.8 of a chocolate! This issue can arise when using linear programming methods to solve problems about discrete variables, which require whole-number solutions, and will be addressed more fully in the next section.

EXERCISE 5B

1 Solve the following linear programming (LP) problem.

Maximise $\quad P = x + 2y$
subject to $\quad 4x + 5y \leqslant 45$
$\quad\quad\quad\quad 4x + 11y \leqslant 44$
$\quad\quad\quad\quad x + y \leqslant 6.$

2 A farmer grows two crops: wheat and beet. The number of hectares of wheat, $x$, and the number of hectares of beet, $y$, must satisfy

$$10x + 3y \leqslant 52$$
$$2x + 3y \leqslant 18$$
$$y \leqslant 4.$$

Determine the values of $x$ and $y$ for which the profit function, $P = 7x + 8y$ is a maximum. State the maximum value of $P$.

**3** A robot can walk at $1.5\,\text{ms}^{-1}$ or run at $4\,\text{ms}^{-1}$. It consumes power at 1 unit per metre when walking, and at three times this rate when running. If its batteries are charged to 9000 units, what is the greatest distance it can cover in half an hour?

**4** A material manufacturer has to decide how much of each of two types of cloth to produce. Each metre of cloth A requires $2\,\text{kg}$ of wool, $\frac{1}{2}$ litre of dye, 5 minutes of loom time, and 4 minutes of worker time. Each metre produces a profit of £3.

Cloth type B requires $1\,\text{kg}$ of wool, $\frac{1}{3}$ litre of dye, 4 minutes of loom time, and 5 minutes of worker time. Each metre produces a profit of £2.50.

The manufacturer has available 6 hours of loom time and 6 hours of worker time for the rest of the day. There are $100\,\text{kg}$ of wool and 28 litres of dye.

**(a)** Show that the constraint on loom time is redundant.

**(b)** Find out how much of each cloth type the manufacturer should produce to maximise her profit.

**5** A paper manufacturer has a roll of paper to cut up. It is 40 cm wide and 200 m long, and is to be cut along its length to produce widths of 11 cm for toilet rolls, and widths of 24 cm for kitchen rolls.

There are two possible cutting plans, both of which may be used on the same roll.

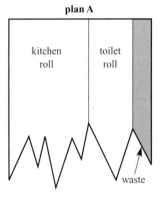

plan A

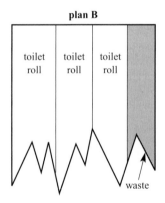

plan B

Kitchen roll paper sells for 7p a metre. Toilet roll paper sells for 4p a metre. Any of the roll that remains uncut can be sold for 8p a metre.

The manufacturer is keen to ensure that no more than 15% of the roll is wasted.

**(a)** Let $a$ metres be the length that is cut to plan A, and $b$ metres be the length cut to plan B, so that $200 - a - b$ metres remains uncut.
Formulate a linear program to find the length of roll which should be cut to each plan so as to produce the maximum income within the given constraints.

**(b)** Solve the problem.

**6** James Bond is very particular about his cocktails. He has them mixed from gin and martini and he insists that they satisfy the following constraints.

**Dryness**

Gin has a dryness rating of 1 and martini a dryness rating of 3. Dryness blends linearly, i.e. a mixture of $x$ ml of gin and $y$ ml of martini has a dryness of

$$\frac{x + 3y}{x + y}.$$

James insists that the dryness of his cocktail is less than or equal to 2.

**Alcohol**

Gin is 45% alcohol by volume. Martini is 15%. Alcohol also blends linearly. James insists that his cocktail is between 18% and 36% alcohol.

James has ordered a 200 ml cocktail. Let the amount of gin in it be $x$ ml, and let the amount of martini be $y$ ml, so that $x + y = 200$.

**(a)** Explain why the dryness constraint may be expressed as $x + 3y \leqslant 400$.

**(b)** In a similar way, produce and simplify two further constraints.

**(c)** Graph all three constraints.

**(d)** Given that gin is more expensive than martini, and remembering that $x + y$ must equal 200, give the cheapest and most expensive cocktails that will satisfy James's requirements.

**(e)** An alternative approach to this problem is to let $p$ be the *proportion* of gin in the cocktail, so that $1 - p$ is the proportion of martini. Using this approach the first constraint becomes $p + 3(1 - p) \leqslant 2$, i.e. $p \geqslant \frac{1}{2}$.

Express the other constraints in this way and compare the acceptable values for $x$ with those that you obtained for $x$ in part **(d)**.

[Oxford] Please note that this question is NOT from the live examinations for the current specification

# LINEAR PROGRAMMING WITH INTEGER SOLUTIONS

In Exercise 5B the problems were all chosen to contain continuous variables; in practice, however, it is very often the case that we require a solution to consist of whole number (integer) values only.

If the linear programming solution, found by the 'ruler' or 'vertex' method, consists just of whole numbers anyway, then there is no difficulty. If not, then it is necessary to search through possible integer solutions inside the feasible region. In the case of a 2-D graphical linear programming question, you could use the 'ruler' method, and your solution would be the last (or first) integer point still inside the feasible region. The 'vertex' method is less reliable for this type of problem.

### EXAMPLE 5.3

A landscaping project involves an area of 2000 m². Trees cost £30 each and require 30 m² of space. Shrubs cost £9 each and need 4 m² of space. At least 75 shrubs must be planted, and £3700 is available to be spent. Trees are thought to be five times as beneficial to wildlife as are shrubs. How many trees and shrubs should be planted to maximise the environmental benefit?

*Solution*

Let $x$ be the number of trees planted.
Let $y$ be the number of shrubs planted.

Maximise      $5x + y$          (environmental benefit)
subject to      $30x + 9y \leqslant 3700$      (cost constraint)
                    $30x + 4y \leqslant 2000$      (space constraint)
                              $y \geqslant 75$        (shrubs constraint)
                              $x \geqslant 0$        (non-negative constraint)
                              $y \geqslant 0$        (non-negative constraint).

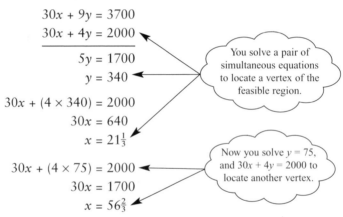

$$30x + 9y = 3700$$
$$\underline{30x + 4y = 2000}$$
$$5y = 1700$$
$$y = 340$$

You solve a pair of simultaneous equations to locate a vertex of the feasible region.

$$30x + (4 \times 340) = 2000$$
$$30x = 640$$
$$x = 21\tfrac{1}{3}$$

Now you solve $y = 75$, and $30x + 4y = 2000$ to locate another vertex.

$$30x + (4 \times 75) = 2000$$
$$30x = 1700$$
$$x = 56\tfrac{2}{3}$$

In figure 5.6 the value of the objective function, the environmental benefit, has been marked at the vertices of the feasible region.

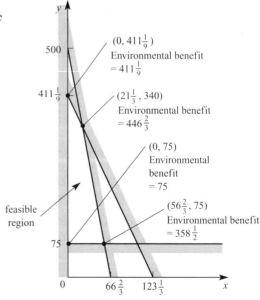

$(0, 411\tfrac{1}{9})$
Environmental benefit $= 411\tfrac{1}{9}$

$(21\tfrac{1}{3}, 340)$
Environmental benefit $= 446\tfrac{2}{3}$

$(0, 75)$
Environmental benefit $= 75$

$(56\tfrac{2}{3}, 75)$
Environmental benefit $= 358\tfrac{1}{2}$

feasible region

FIGURE 5.6

So the solution is $x = 21\frac{1}{3}$, $y = 340$ with an environmental benefit measure of $446\frac{2}{3}$. The obvious integer point to check is (21, 340), since this is clearly feasible, and is near to $(21\frac{1}{3}, 340)$. It gives an environmental benefit of 445. But you can do (a little) better!

The point (21, 341) is in the feasible region since

$$(30 \times 21) + (9 \times 341) = 630 + 3069 = 3699 < 3700.$$

This gives an environmental benefit of 446, and this is the (or at least an) optimal solution for this problem since 446 is the integer part of the solution. Had this not been the case then the optimal point might possibly have been considerably further away from the optimal point.

So the solution to the problem is to plant 21 trees and 341 shrubs.

EXERCISE 5C

1  A builder can build either luxury houses or standard houses on a plot of land. Planning regulations prevent the builder from building more than 30 houses altogether, and he wants to build at least 5 luxury houses and at least 10 standard houses. Each luxury house requires $300\,m^2$ of land, and each standard house requires $150\,m^2$ of land. The total area of the plot is $6500\,m^2$.

   Given that the profit on a luxury house is £14 000 and that the profit on a standard house is £9000, find how many of each type of house he should build to maximise his profit.

2  A company manufactures two types of container, each requiring the same amount of material. The first type of container requires 4 seconds on a cutting machine and 3 seconds on a sewing machine.

   The second type of container requires 2 seconds on the cutting machine and 7 seconds on the sewing machine. Each machine is available for 1 hour. The first type of container gives a profit of 40p. The second type gives a profit of 30p. How many of each type should be made to maximise profit?

3  A car park with total usable area $300\,m^2$ is to have spaces marked out for small cars and for large cars. A small car space has area $10\,m^2$ and a large car space has area $12\,m^2$. The ratio of small cars to large cars parked at any one time is estimated to be between $2:3$ and $2:1$. Find the number of spaces of each type that should be provided so as to maximise the number of cars that can be parked.

**4** Solve the following LP.

$$\text{Maximise} \qquad z = x + y$$
$$\text{subject to} \qquad 3x + 4y \leqslant 12$$
$$2x + y \leqslant 4$$
$$x \text{ integer}$$
$$y \text{ integer.}$$

**5** A factory produces sprockets and widgets. Sprockets need 10 minutes of labour each, 15 minutes of machine time, and £20 of materials. Widgets need 20 minutes of labour each, 10 minutes of machine time and £30 of materials. For the next day there are 18 hours of labour, 20 hours of machine time and £2000 of materials.

Given that the objective is to manufacture as many completed items as possible, find how many sprockets and how many widgets should be produced.

**6** A baker has 8.5 kg of flour, 5.5 kg of butter and 5 kg of sugar available at the end of a working day. With these ingredients, biscuits and/or buns can be made. The recipes are as follows:

30 biscuits    200 g flour                40 buns    200 g flour
               120 g butter                          200 g butter
               100 g sugar                           200 g sugar

**(a)** Biscuits are sold for 5p each and buns for 7p each. Let $x$ be the number of biscuits baked and $y$ be the number of buns baked. Assuming that any number of biscuits and/or buns can be baked, show that the amount of flour used (in g) is given by $6\frac{2}{3}x + 5y$.

Hence write down and simplify an inequality constraining the values of $x$ and $y$.

**(b)** Produce two further inequalities relating to the availability of butter and of sugar.

**(c)** Assuming that all biscuits and buns can be sold, produce a function which gives the income from the sales.

**(d)** Formulate and solve the linear program:
*Maximise income subject to the availability of flour, butter and sugar.*
Assuming it is possible to make part-batches, state the maximum income expected, and the numbers of biscuits and buns baked.

[Oxford] Please note that this question is NOT from the live examinations for the current specification

# MINIMISATION

So far, all of the problems have required finding the maximum value of the objective function within the feasible region. Minimisation problems can be solved graphically using exactly the same approach.

### EXAMPLE 5.4

An oil company has two refineries. Refinery 1 produces 100 barrels of high grade oil, 200 barrels of medium grade oil, and 300 barrels of low grade oil per day. It costs £10 000 per day to operate.

Refinery 2 produces 200 barrels of high grade oil, 100 barrels of medium grade oil and 200 barrels of low grade oil per day. It costs £9000 per day to operate.

An order is received for 2000 barrels of high grade oil, 2000 barrels of medium grade oil and 3600 barrels of low grade oil. For how many days should each refinery be operated to fill the order at least cost?

*Solution*

Let $x$ be the number of days for which refinery 1 is operated.
Let $y$ be the number of days for which refinery 2 is operated.

High grade oil produced = $100x + 200y$
so you require $100x + 200y \geqslant 2000$.

Medium grade oil produced = $200x + 100y$
so you require $200x + 100y \geqslant 2000$.

Low grade oil produced = $300x + 200y$
so you require $300x + 200y \geqslant 3600$.

Cost = $10\,000x + 9000y$.

So the LP is:

minimise $\qquad 10\,000x + 9000y$
subject to $\qquad 100x + 200y \geqslant 2000$
$\qquad\qquad\quad 200x + 100y \geqslant 2000$
$\qquad\qquad\quad 300x + 200y \geqslant 3600$
$\qquad\qquad\quad x \geqslant 0, y \geqslant 0.$

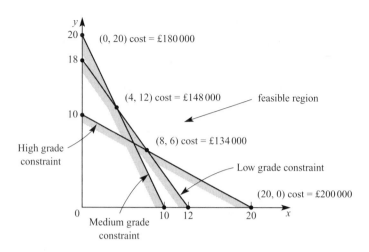

FIGURE 5.7

In this case, the feasible region is unbounded above but, because you have a minimisation objective, the solution will still be at one of the vertices.

Note that (4, 12) is found by solving simultaneously

$$200x + 100y = 2000$$
$$\text{and} \quad 300x + 200y = 3600,$$

and (8, 6) is found by solving simultaneously

$$100x + 200y = 2000$$
$$\text{and} \quad 300x + 200y = 3600.$$

The solution is to operate refinery 1 for eight days and refinery 2 for six days at a cost of £134 000.

EXERCISE 5D

1 A food company is designing a new product using wheatgerm and oat flour. Nutritional requirements must be met.

Each ounce of wheatgerm contains 2 milligrams of niacin, 3 milligrams of iron and 0.5 milligrams of thiamin, and costs 8p.

Each ounce of oat flour contains 3 milligrams of niacin, 3 milligrams of iron, 0.25 milligrams of thiamin, and costs 5p.

A portion of the product must contain at least 7 milligrams of niacin, 8 milligrams of iron, and 1 milligram of thiamin.

How much of each ingredient should be used in a portion to satisfy the nutritional requirements at least cost?

2 A vet is treating a farm animal. He must provide minimum daily requirements of an antibiotic, a vitamin and a nutrient. He has two types of medicine available, tablets and liquid.

The table summarises what the medicines contain and the requirements.

|  | Antibiotic | Vitamin | Nutrient |
|---|---|---|---|
| Tablets (units per tablet) | 3 | 2 | 10 |
| Liquid (units per dose) | 2 | 4 | 50 |
| Daily requirement (units) | 18 | 16 | 100 |

(a) If $x$ is the number of tablets which the vet prescribes per day, and $y$ is the number of doses of liquid medicine, explain why $3x + 2y$ must not be less than 18.

Draw the inequality $3x + 2y \geq 18$ on a graph, with each axis labelled from 0 to 10.

(b) Construct inequalities in terms of $x$ and $y$ relating to daily vitamin and nutrient requirements.

Draw these two inequalities on your graph.

The tablets cost £0.38 each and liquid medicine costs £1 per dose. The vet wants to find the cheapest way to treat the animal.

(c) Solve the linear programming problem, allowing $x$ and $y$ to take any values.

(d) Solve the problem when $x$ and $y$ must be integers.

(e) Which solution should the vet adopt and why?

[MEI]

3 The contract conditions imposed by a coach company on hiring out a minibus are as follows.

- The total number of passengers must not exceed 14.
- The total number of passengers must not be less than 10.
- Children pay £5 each.
- Adults pay £10 each.
- There must be at least as many full-fare passengers as half-fare passengers.

Find the maximum and minimum amounts the company can receive for the hire of its minibus.

4 A manufacturing company has a production plan in which at least 500 units are to be produced each week. The company employs two categories of employee: category A and category B. Category A employees are paid £265 per week and they each produce 13 units per week. Category B employees are paid £205 per week and each produces 10 units per week. Company policy is to have at least 45 employees producing these units.

(a) Write down a linear program to find the optimal mix of employees at the cheapest cost.

(b) Use a graphical approach to solve your linear programming problem, ignoring for the moment the fact that the solution to the problem must be integer.

(c) The best *integer* solution to the problem incurs a weekly pay bill of £10 235. Find this solution.

(d) Compare and contrast the linear problem in part (b) and the integer problem in part (c), the solutions, and their associated costs.

[AEB] Please note that this question is NOT from the live examinations for the current specification

5 Joan is producing a revision plan for the weekend for two subject areas, A and B. She has at most six hours available. She feels that she needs to work for at least two hours on each subject area. The subject areas contribute 60% and 40% respectively in the coming examination, and Joan intends to reflect that balance in the time that she allocates to revising for each area.

(a) Define appropriate variables and formulate four constraints (three *inequalities* and one *equality*) to model Joan's requirements.

(b) Illustrate your constraints graphically. Indicate the feasible points and show that one of the constraints is redundant.

(c) Produce alternative revision plans which satisfy the constraints and which use
   (i)   as much time as possible
   (ii)  as little time as possible.

An alternative approach to solving this problem is to use the equality constraint to replace one variable by the other in each inequality, thus reducing the problem to one involving a single variable only.

(d) Solve the problem by this approach, comparing the answer with that from part (c).

# THE SIMPLEX ALGORITHM AND TABLEAU

So far you have considered only two-dimensional problems, i.e. those in which there have been two variables. Many practical problems actually contain three (or more) variables.

An ingenious way of dealing with inequalities in linear programming problems is to introduce the idea of a slack variable. This is an artificial quantity that literally takes up the slack, turning an inequality into an equation. For example, the inequality

$$10x + 15y + 20z \leqslant 300$$

may be replaced with the equation

$$10x + 15y + 20z + r = 300$$

where $r$ is a slack variable.

The use of slack variables leads to a method of solution known as the simplex algorithm. It may be used for problems with any number of variables, but is particularly helpful in formulating problems in three variables, when the graphical methods break down. The Edexcel A level specification requires you to know how to use the simplex method for up to three variables with three non-trivial constraints.

---

**EXAMPLE 5.5**

Using the simplex method, maximise $P = x + 0.8y$ subject to the constraints

$$x + y \leqslant 1000$$
$$2x + y \leqslant 1500$$
$$3x + 2y \leqslant 2400.$$

*Solution*

**Step 1: Formulate the problem using slack variables.**
The three inequalities may be rewritten as

$$x + y + r = 1000$$
$$2x + y + s = 1500$$
$$3x + 2y + t = 2400$$

where $r$, $s$ and $t$ are three slack variables.

Also, the objective function is written as $P - x - 0.8y = 0$

Writing these equations in full, you have

$$1x + 1y + 1r + 0s + 0t = 1000$$
$$2x + 1y + 0r + 1s + 0t = 1500$$
$$3x + 2y + 0r + 0s + 1t = 2400$$
$$P - 1x - 0.8y + 0r + 0s + 0t = 0.$$

## Step 2: Construct an initial tableau.

The information in the equations is now transferred into a table, known as a *Simplex tableau*.

The coefficients of the variables $x$, $y$, $r$, $s$ and $t$ go in the main body of the table and the total values go at the right-hand side. Initially the 'basic value' column contains the slack variables $r$, $s$ and $t$ and the objective function, $P$.

| Basic variable | $x$ | $y$ | $r$ | $s$ | $t$ | Value |
|---|---|---|---|---|---|---|
| $r$ | 1 | 1 | 1 | 0 | 0 | 1000 |
| $s$ | 2 | 1 | 0 | 1 | 0 | 1500 |
| $t$ | 3 | 2 | 0 | 0 | 1 | 2400 |
| $P$ | −1 | −0.8 | 0 | 0 | 0 | 0 |

## Step 3: Check for optimality.

Look at the coefficients at the foot of the tableau, in the objective function row. When an optimum solution has been found, the basic variables have zero coefficients and the others are non-negative.

| Basic variable | $x$ | $y$ | $r$ | $s$ | $t$ | Value |
|---|---|---|---|---|---|---|
| $r$ | 1 | 1 | 1 | 0 | 0 | 1000 |
| $s$ | 2 | 1 | 0 | 1 | 0 | 1500 |
| $t$ | 3 | 2 | 0 | 0 | 1 | 2400 |
| $P$ | −1 | −0.8 | 0 | 0 | 0 | 0 |

These coefficients are indeed zero . . .

. . . but these are *not* non-negative . . .

. . . so an optimum solution has *not* yet been achieved.

## Step 4: Identify the pivotal column.

Look again at the coefficients at the foot of the tableau, and select the most negative one: in this case −1. This identifies the *pivotal column*.

| Basic variable | $x$ | $y$ | $r$ | $s$ | $t$ | Value |
|---|---|---|---|---|---|---|
| $r$ | 1 | 1 | 1 | 0 | 0 | 1000 |
| $s$ | 2 | 1 | 0 | 1 | 0 | 1500 |
| $t$ | 3 | 2 | 0 | 0 | 1 | 2400 |
| $P$ | −1 | −0.8 | 0 | 0 | 0 | 0 |

**Step 5: Identify the pivotal row.**

For each row except the bottom one, you compute an index known as the *theta value ($\theta$)*, which is simply the value in the final column divided by the corresponding entry in the pivotal column. For example, in the second row, $1500 \div 2 = 750$.

Now take the lowest positive theta value, and use that to select the *pivotal row*. The pivotal row will intersect the pivotal column to locate the cell acting as the *pivot*, in this case, 2.

pivot

| Basic variable | $x$ | $y$ | $r$ | $s$ | $t$ | Value | $\theta$ |
|---|---|---|---|---|---|---|---|
| $r$ | 1 | 1 | 1 | 0 | 0 | 1000 | 1000 |
| $s$ | 2 | 1 | 0 | 1 | 0 | 1500 | 750 |
| $t$ | 3 | 2 | 0 | 0 | 1 | 2400 | 800 |
| $P$ | −1 | −0.8 | 0 | 0 | 0 | 0 | |

**Step 6: Rescale the pivotal row so the pivot takes a value of 1.**

In this case the pivot is presently 2, so you simply divide every entry in the pivotal row by 2. You also switch the basic variable at the start of the row to the variable indicated by the pivotal row. In this case you replace $s$ in the second row by $x$.

This notation indicates you have divided row 2 by 2.

| Basic variable | $x$ | $y$ | $r$ | $s$ | $t$ | Value | |
|---|---|---|---|---|---|---|---|
| $r$ | 1 | 1 | 1 | 0 | 0 | 1000 | |
| $x$ | 1 | 0.5 | 0 | 0.5 | 0 | 750 | $R_2 \div 2$ |
| $t$ | 3 | 2 | 0 | 0 | 1 | 2400 | |
| $P$ | −1 | −0.8 | 0 | 0 | 0 | 0 | |

**Step 7: Add or subtract a multiple of the pivotal row to each other row in turn, in such a way as to create a column of zeros in the non-pivotal rows of the pivotal column.**

For example, the new $r$ row is the old one minus the pivotal row. The new $t$ row is the old one minus three times the pivotal row. Remember to include the value column in the calculation, too.

These operations should be indicated at the end of each row by $R_1 - R_2$, $R_3 - 3R_2$, etc.

| Basic variable | $x$ | $y$ | $r$ | $s$ | $t$ | Value | |
|---|---|---|---|---|---|---|---|
| $r$ | 0 | 0.5 | 1 | –0.5 | 0 | 250 | $R_1 - R_2$ |
| $x$ | 1 | 0.5 | 0 | 0.5 | 0 | 750 | |
| $t$ | 0 | 0.5 | 0 | –1.5 | 1 | 150 | $R_3 - 3R_2$ |
| $P$ | 0 | –0.3 | 0 | 0.5 | 0 | 750 | $R_4 + R_2$ |

**Step 8: Analyse the tableau.**

This tableau shows that it is possible to allow $P$ to take a value of 750. You now check again to see if this is an optimal solution. If not, you repeat steps 4 to 8 as necessary, until an optimal solution is achieved.

There is a negative value, –0.3, in the bottom row. This tells you the optimal solution has not been achieved.

**Repeat steps 4 and 5: Identify the pivotal column and pivotal row.**

pivot

| Basic variable | $x$ | $y$ | $r$ | $s$ | $t$ | Value | $\theta$ |
|---|---|---|---|---|---|---|---|
| $r$ | 0 | 0.5 | 1 | –0.5 | 0 | 250 | 500 |
| $x$ | 1 | 0.5 | 0 | 0.5 | 0 | 750 | 1500 |
| $t$ | 0 | 0.5 | 0 | –1.5 | 1 | 150 | 300 |
| $P$ | 0 | –0.3 | 0 | 0.5 | 0 | 750 | |

**Repeat step 6: Resale the pivotal row, so the pivot takes a value of 1.**

| Basic variable | $x$ | $y$ | $r$ | $s$ | $t$ | Value | |
|---|---|---|---|---|---|---|---|
| $r$ | 0 | 0.5 | 1 | –0.5 | 0 | 250 | |
| $x$ | 1 | 0.5 | 0 | 0.5 | 0 | 750 | |
| $y$ | 0 | 1 | 0 | –3 | 2 | 300 | $R_3 \div 0.5$ |
| $P$ | 0 | –0.3 | 0 | 0.5 | 0 | 750 | |

Notice that you change the basic variable for this row from $t$ to $y$.

**Repeat step 7: Add or subtract a multiple of the pivotal row to each other row in turn, in such a way as to create a column of zeros in the non-pivotal rows of the pivotal column.**

| Basic variable | $x$ | $y$ | $r$ | $s$ | $t$ | Value | |
|---|---|---|---|---|---|---|---|
| $r$ | 0 | 0 | 1 | 1 | −1 | 100 | $R_1 - 0.5R_3$ |
| $x$ | 1 | 0 | 0 | 2 | −1 | 600 | $R_2 - 0.5R_3$ |
| $y$ | 0 | 1 | 0 | −3 | 2 | 300 | |
| $P$ | 0 | 0 | 0 | −0.4 | 0.6 | 840 | $R_4 + 0.3R_3$ |

**Repeat step 8.**
This tableau shows that it is possible to allow $P$ to take a value of 840, as compared with 750 on the previous iteration. It is still not an optimal solution, however, as can be seen from the value of −0.4 in the bottom row, so you run through steps 4 to 7 one more time.

**Repeat steps 4 and 5.**
Notice that the theta values include −100, but that you ignore this when selecting the pivotal row; you choose the smallest *positive* theta value.

| Basic variable | $x$ | $y$ | $r$ | $s$ | $t$ | Value | $\theta$ |
|---|---|---|---|---|---|---|---|
| $r$ | 0 | 0 | 1 | 1 | −1 | 100 | 100 |
| $x$ | 1 | 0 | 0 | 2 | −1 | 600 | 300 |
| $y$ | 0 | 1 | 0 | −3 | 2 | 300 | −100 |
| $P$ | 0 | 0 | 0 | −0.4 | 0.6 | 840 | |

**Repeat step 6.**
There is no need to rescale, as the pivot already has a value of 1. However, you change the basic variable for this row from $r$ to $s$.

| Basic variable | $x$ | $y$ | $r$ | $s$ | $t$ | Value |
|---|---|---|---|---|---|---|
| $s$ | 0 | 0 | 1 | 1 | −1 | 100 |
| $x$ | 1 | 0 | 0 | 2 | −1 | 600 |
| $y$ | 0 | 1 | 0 | −3 | 2 | 300 |
| $P$ | 0 | 0 | 0 | −0.4 | 0.6 | 840 |

**Repeat step 7.**

| Basic variable | $x$ | $y$ | $r$ | $s$ | $t$ | Value | |
|:---:|:---:|:---:|:---:|:---:|:---:|:---:|:---:|
| $s$ | 0 | 0 | 1 | 1 | −1 | 100 | |
| $x$ | 1 | 0 | −2 | 0 | 1 | 400 | $R_2 - 2R_1$ |
| $y$ | 0 | 1 | 3 | 0 | −1 | 600 | $R_3 + 3R_1$ |
| $P$ | 0 | 0 | 0.4 | 0 | 0.2 | 880 | $R_4 + 0.4R_1$ |

**Repeat step 8.**

Now optimality has been achieved, because

- there are zeros in the bottom row corresponding to the columns for the basic variables $s$, $x$ and $y$
- the two other entries are non-negative (0.4 and 0.2).

**Step 9: Interpret the tableau.**

The tableau can now be interpreted you look at the entries in the basic variable column and the corresponding entries in the value column. These tell you that the solution occurs when $x = 400$ and $y = 600$. The value of $P$ is then 880.

The value of $s = 100$ tells you that there are 100 units of slack in the second constraint.

You can compute the value of the slack variable $r$.

$$r = 1000 - x - y \quad \longleftarrow \quad \text{from the original inequality}$$
$$= 1000 - 400 - 600$$
$$= 0$$

Similarly

using the values of $x$ and $y$ from the final tableau

$$t = 2400 - 3x - 2y$$
$$= 2400 - 3 \times 400 - 2 \times 600$$
$$= 0.$$

This tells you that the two corresponding constraints are at their limit, with no slack.

In the examination you will usually be asked to give the value of $P$ and each of the variables $x$, $y$, $r$, $s$ and $t$. You should be able to state the implications of the values of the slack variables.

So far, you have seen the simplex algorithm used purely as a procedure, without looking at its meaning. To understand what the iterations are achieving, it is perhaps informative to consider Example 5.5 again, but from a graphical point of view.

The constraints and the feasible region for Example 5.5 are shown in figure 5.8.

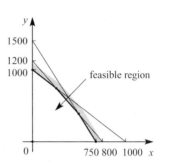

FIGURE 5.8

The initial simplex tableau gave a *P* value of zero, clearly not an optimal value! As you worked through the algorithm, improved values of 750 and 840 were obtained, but these still did not pass the optimality check. Finally you obtained a value of 880, and that was shown to be optimal.

So, in effect, the simplex tableau is imitating the behaviour of the graphical vertex method, by visiting the vertices of the feasible region.

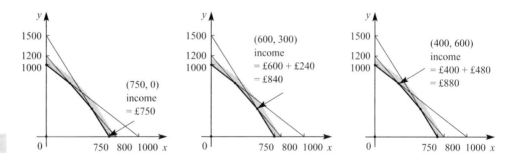

FIGURE 5.9

A three-dimensional problem may have inequalities in, for example, *x*, *y* and *z* and the simplex tableau method may be extended to deal with such problems and, indeed, problems in more than three dimensions. However, the graphical method cannot practically be used beyond two dimensions.

EXERCISE 5E

**1** Use the simplex algorithm to solve the following LP.

Maximise $P = 16x + 24y$
subject to $2x + 3y \leq 24$
$2x + y \leq 16$
$y \leq 6$
$x \geq 0, y \geq 0.$

129

2 Use the simplex algorithm to solve the following LP.

Maximise    $P = 9x + 10y + 6z$
subject to    $2x + 3y + 4z \leqslant 3$
$6x + 6y + 2z \leqslant 8$
$x \geqslant 0, y \geqslant 0, z \geqslant 0.$

3 Use the simplex algorithm to solve the following LP.

Maximise    $P = 3w + 2x$
subject to    $w + x + y + z \leqslant 150$
$2w + x + 3y + 4z \leqslant 200$
$w \geqslant 0, x \geqslant 0, y \geqslant 0, z \geqslant 0.$

4 Use the simplex algorithm to solve the following LP.

Maximise    $P = 3w + 2x$
subject to    $w + x + y + z \leqslant 150$
$2w + x + 3y + 4z \leqslant 200$
$w \geqslant x$ (rewrite this as $x - w \leqslant 0$)
$w \geqslant 0, x \geqslant 0, y \geqslant 0, z \geqslant 0.$

5 In an executive initiative course, participants are asked to travel as far as possible in three hours using a combination of moped, car and lorry. The moped can be carried in the car and the car can be carried on the lorry.

The moped travels at 20 miles per hour (mph) with a petrol consumption of 60 miles per gallon (mpg). The car travels at 40 mph with a petrol consumption of 40 mpg. The lorry travels at 30 mph with a petrol consumption of 20 mpg.

2.5 gallons of petrol are available.

The moped must not be used for more than 55 miles, and a total of no more than 55 miles must be covered using the car and/or lorry.

(a) Formulate the above specifications as a linear programming problem, stating clearly your choice of variables and your objective function.
(b) Set up a simplex tableau to solve the problem.
(c) Perform two iterations of the simplex algorithm.
(d) Is the tableau resulting from part (c) optimal?
What strategy is indicated by the tableau, and how much time and petrol would be used?

[Oxford] Please note that this question is NOT from the live examinations for the current specification

EXERCISE 5F EXAMINATION-STYLE QUESTIONS

1 An airline needs to decide how many rows of seats in its new plane will be club class, and how many will be economy class. The plane can have up to 30 rows of seats in total. Every club class row has 4 seats and every economy class row has 6 seats.

The airline does not believe that it can sell more than 10 rows of club class seats.

Club class tickets sell at 25% above the price of economy class tickets.

On long flights the plane can carry no more than 150 passengers.

The airline wishes to maximise its income from ticket sales.

(a) Explain why this can be formulated as the following linear programming problem.

$$\text{Maximise} \quad 5x + 6y$$
$$\text{subject to} \quad x + y \leqslant 30$$
$$4x + 6y \leqslant 150$$
$$x \leqslant 10$$
$$x \geqslant 0, y \geqslant 0.$$

(b) Solve the problem graphically.

(c) On short flights less fuel is needed and the plane can carry more passengers. What must be the capacity of the plane if the constraint $x + y \leqslant 30$ is not redundant?

[MEI]

2 A company bottles and sells mountain spring water. It produces one-litre bottles which sell for 50p, and half-litre bottles which sell for 30p.

The spring produces 5000 litres per day.

There is a demand for up to 4000 one-litre bottles per day, and up to 3000 half-litre bottles per day.

The company wishes to maximise its income from the sale of bottles of water.

(a) Choose variables for the number of one-litre bottles the company should produce per day, and the number of half-litre bottles.

Write down an expression for the daily income in terms of your variables.

Write down an inequality which models the constraint imposed by the availability of spring water.

Complete the formulation of a linear programming problem to find how many of each type of bottle the company should produce per day. You will need two more inequalities for this.

(b) Use a graphical method to solve the problem.

(c) The company's marketing manager advises that half-litre bottles be reduced in price to 28p to increase demand for half-litre bottles. Verify that the company must sell more than 5000 half-litre bottles per day for income to be increased.

(d) After a wet winter the spring produces more water. At the original prices, how much extra water per day could the company use, and how much extra income would this generate?

[MEI]

3 A recipe for jam states that the weight of sugar used must be between the weight of fruit used and four-thirds of the weight of fruit used. Georgia has 10 kg of fruit available and 11 kg of sugar.

(a) Define two variables and formulate inequalities in those variables to model this information.

(b) Draw a graph to represent your inequalities and label the feasible region.

(c) Find the vertices of your feasible region and identify the points which would represent the best mix of ingredients under each of the following circumstances.

   (i) There is to be as much jam as possible, given that the weight of jam produced is the sum of the weights of the fruit and the sugar.

   (ii) There is to be as much jam as possible, given that it is to have the lowest possible proportion of sugar.

   (iii) Fruit costs £1 per kilogram, sugar costs 50p per kilogram and the objective is to produce as much jam as possible within a budget of £15.

[MEI]

4 A chemical company produces two products $X$ and $Y$. Based on potential demand, the total production each week must be at least 380 gallons. A major customer's weekly order for 125 gallons of $Y$ must be satisfied.

Product $X$ requires 2 hours of processing time for each gallon and product $Y$ requires 4 hours of processing time for each gallon. There are 1200 hours of processing time available each week. Let $x$ be the number of gallons of $X$ produced and $y$ be the number of gallons of $Y$ produced each week.

(a) Write down the inequalities which $x$ and $y$ must satisfy.

It costs £3 to produce 1 gallon of $X$ and £2 to produce 1 gallon of $Y$. Given that the total cost of production is £$C$,

(b) express $C$ in terms of $x$ and $y$.

The company wishes to minimise the total cost.

(c) Using the graphical method, solve the resulting linear programming problem. Find the optimal values of $x$ and $y$ and the resulting total cost.

(d) Find the maximum cost of production for all possible choices of $x$ and $y$ which satisfy the inequalities you wrote down in part (a).

[Edexcel]

**5** Two fertilisers are available, a liquid $X$ and a powder $Y$. A bottle of $X$ contains 5 units of chemical $A$, 2 units of chemical $B$ and $\frac{1}{2}$ unit of chemical $C$. A packet of $Y$ contains 1 unit of $A$, 2 units of $B$ and 2 units of $C$. A professional gardener makes her own fertiliser. She requires at least 10 units of $A$, at least 12 units of $B$ and at least 6 units of $C$.

She buys $x$ bottles of $X$ and $y$ packets of $Y$.

**(a)** Write down the inequalities which model this situation.

**(b)** Draw a graph to represent these inequalities and label the feasible region.

A bottle of $X$ costs £2 and a packet of $Y$ costs £3.

**(c)** Write down an expression, in terms of $x$ and $y$, for the total cost £$T$.

**(d)** Using your graph, obtain the values of $x$ and $y$ that give the minimum value of $T$. Make your method clear and calculate the minimum value of $T$.

**(e)** Suggest how the situation might be changed so that it could no longer be represented graphically.

[Edexcel]

**6** A tailor makes two types of garment, $A$ and $B$. He has available $70\,\text{m}^2$ of cotton fabric and $90\,\text{m}^2$ of woollen fabric. Garment $A$ requires $1\,\text{m}^2$ of cotton fabric and $3\,\text{m}^2$ of woollen fabric. Garment $B$ requires $2\,\text{m}^2$ of each fabric.

The tailor makes $x$ garments of type $A$ and $y$ garments of type $B$.

**(a)** Explain why this can be modelled by the following inequalities.

$$x + 2y \leqslant 70$$
$$3x + 2y \leqslant 90$$
$$x \geqslant 0, y \geqslant 0.$$

The tailor sells type $A$ for £30 and type $B$ for £40. All garments made are sold. The tailor wishes to maximise his total income.

**(b)** Set up an initial simplex tableau for this problem.

**(c)** Solve the problem using the simplex algorithm.

The diagram shows a graphical representation of the feasible region for this problem.

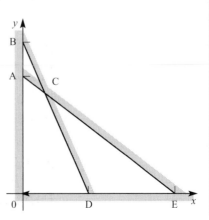

**(d)** Obtain the coordinates of the points $A$, $C$ and $D$.

**(e)** Relate each stage of the simplex algorithm to the corresponding point in the diagram.

[Edexcel]

**7** While solving a maximising linear programming problem, the following tableau was obtained.

| Basic variable | $x$ | $y$ | $z$ | $r$ | $s$ | $t$ | Value |
|---|---|---|---|---|---|---|---|
| $r$ | 0 | 0 | $1\frac{2}{3}$ | 1 | 0 | $-\frac{1}{6}$ | $\frac{2}{3}$ |
| $y$ | 0 | 1 | $3\frac{1}{3}$ | 0 | 1 | $-\frac{1}{3}$ | $\frac{1}{3}$ |
| $x$ | 1 | 0 | $-3$ | 0 | $-1$ | $\frac{1}{2}$ | 1 |
| $P$ | 0 | 0 | 1 | 0 | 1 | 1 | 11 |

(a) Explain why this is an optimal tableau.

(b) Write down the optimal solution of this problem, stating the value of every variable.

(c) Write down the profit equation from the tableau. Use it to explain why changing the value of any of the non-basic variables will decrease the value of $P$.

[Edexcel]

**8** A chemical company makes three products, X, Y and Z. It wishes to maximise its profit £$P$. The manager considers the limitations on the raw materials available and models the situation with the following linear programming problem.

$$\begin{aligned}
\text{Maximise} \quad & P = 3x + 6y + 4z \\
\text{subject to} \quad & x + z \leqslant 4 \\
& x + 4y + 2z \leqslant 6 \\
& x + y + 2z \leqslant 12 \\
& x \geqslant 0, y \geqslant 0, z \geqslant 0
\end{aligned}$$

where $x$, $y$ and $z$ are the weights, in kilograms, of products X, Y and Z respectively.

A possible initial tableau is shown below.

| Basic variable | $x$ | $y$ | $z$ | $r$ | $s$ | $t$ | Value |
|---|---|---|---|---|---|---|---|
| $r$ | 1 | 0 | 1 | 1 | 0 | 0 | 4 |
| $s$ | 1 | 4 | 2 | 0 | 1 | 0 | 6 |
| $t$ | 1 | 1 | 2 | 0 | 0 | 1 | 12 |
| $P$ | $-3$ | $-6$ | $-4$ | 0 | 0 | 0 | 0 |

(a) Explain
  (i) the purpose of the variables $r$, $s$ and $t$
  (ii) the final row of the tableau.

**(b)** Solve this linear programming problem by using the simplex algorithm. Increase $y$ for your first iteration and then increase $x$ for your second iteration.

**(c)** Interpret your solution.

[Edexcel]

**9** T42 Co. Ltd produces three different blends of tea, Morning, Afternoon and Evening. The teas must be processed, blended and then packed for distribution. The table below shows the time taken, in hours, for each stage of the production of a tonne of tea. It also shows the profit, in hundreds of pounds, on each tonne.

| Tea | Processing | Blending | Packing | Profit (£100) |
|---|---|---|---|---|
| Morning blend | 3 | 1 | 2 | 4 |
| Afternoon blend | 2 | 3 | 4 | 5 |
| Evening blend | 4 | 2 | 3 | 3 |

The total times available each week for processing, blending and packing are 35, 20 and 24 hours respectively. T42 Co. Ltd wishes to maximise the weekly profit.

Let $x$, $y$ and $z$ be the number of tonnes of Morning, Afternoon and Evening blend produced each week.

**(a)** Formulate the above situation as a linear programming problem, listing clearly the objective function and the constraints as inequalities.

An initial simplex tableau for the above situation is shown below.

| Basic variable | $x$ | $y$ | $z$ | $r$ | $s$ | $t$ | Value |
|---|---|---|---|---|---|---|---|
| $r$ | 3 | 2 | 4 | 1 | 0 | 0 | 35 |
| $s$ | 1 | 3 | $\cdot 2$ | 0 | 1 | 0 | 20 |
| $t$ | 2 | 4 | 3 | 0 | 0 | 1 | 24 |
| $P$ | −4 | −5 | −3 | 0 | 0 | 0 | 0 |

**(b)** Solve this linear programming problem using the simplex algorithm. Take the most negative number in the profit row to indicate the pivot column at each stage.

T42 Co. Ltd wishes to increase its profit further and is prepared to increase the time available for processing or blending or packing or any two of these three.

**(c)** Use your answer to part **(b)** to advise the company as to the stages(s) for which it should increase the time available.

[Edexcel]

**10** A production unit makes two types of product, X and Y. Production levels
are measured in tonnes and are constrained by the availability of finance,
staff and storage space. Requirements for, and daily availabilities of, each of
these resources are summarised in the table.

|  | Finance (£) | Staff time (hours) | Storage space (m³) |
|---|---|---|---|
| Requirement per tonne for product X | 200 | 8 | 1 |
| Requirement per tonne for product Y | 100 | 8 | 3 |
| Resources available per day | 1000 | 48 | 15 |

The profit on these products is £160 per tonne for X and £120 per tonne for Y.

**(a)** Express the three resource constraints as inequalities and write two
further inequalities indicating that production levels are non-negative.

**(b)** Given that the objective is to maximise profit, state the objective function.

**(c)** Illustrate the inequalities graphically, and use your graph to find the best
daily production plan.

**(d)** Set up an initial tableau for the problem and use the simplex algorithm to
solve it. Relate each stage of the tableau to its corresponding point on
your graph.

[Oxford] Please note that this question is NOT from
the live examinations for the current specification

## KEY POINTS

1 Linear programming problems may be formulated by the use of inequalities to describe the constraints. All the constraints are satisfied within the feasible region.

2 Linear programming problems typically require finding the maximum profit or minimum cost, for example. The quantity to be maximised or minimised is known as the objective function.

3 Problems in two variables may be solved graphically by using either the ruler method or the vertex method. Problems in two or more variables may also be solved by the simplex tableau method.

4 There are three steps involved in each cycle of the simplex algorithm.
   • Identify a pivot column.
   • Use the theta values to identify the pivot row, and hence the pivot element.
   • Perform row operations to obtain zero values within the pivot column.

   The tableau is then checked for optimality before applying the procedure again if necessary.

5 If the problem involves variables with integer values, then points within the feasible region that are close to a (non-integer) optimal solution can be checked. In two-dimensional graphical problems, use of the ruler method will ensure that the best integer solution is found.

# Chapter six

# MATCHINGS

Artificial intelligence is no match for natural stupidity.

*Anonymous*

## BIPARTITE GRAPHS

A *bipartite graph* is one in which the vertices are separated into two sets.
The edges are drawn to connect a vertex from one set to a vertex in the other.

**EXAMPLE 6.1**

Five friends are discussing their interests in music. Annie likes jazz and rock, Bruno likes rock and classical, Chuck likes classical, Dora likes rock, classical and opera, and Ellen likes classical and opera. Illustrate this information on a bipartite graph.

*Solution*

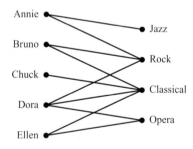

**FIGURE 6.1**

## MATCHINGS

A *matching* is a subgraph of a bipartite graph, such that no vertex is connected to more than one edge.

The example in figure 6.1 is not a matching because Annie, for example, likes both jazz and rock.

**EXAMPLE 6.2**

Ginny has four CDs: one each of jazz, rock, classical and operatic music. She wants to lend them to some of her friends, so that no friend borrows more than one CD. Her friends are Annie, who likes jazz and rock, Bruno, who likes rock and classical, Chuck, who likes classical, Dora, who likes rock, classical and opera, and Ellen, who likes classical and opera. Draw a diagram to show one way in which Ginny might decide to lend out the CDs.

*Solution*

Suppose Ginny decides to lend the classical CD to Chuck, since this is all he likes, and the opera CD to Ellen. Then she might lend the rock CD to Bruno and the jazz CD to Annie, so the matching would look as shown in figure 6.2.

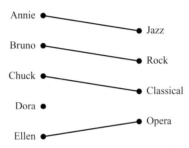

**FIGURE 6.2**

## MAXIMAL MATCHINGS AND COMPLETE MATCHINGS

A *maximal matching* is a matching in which the maximum number of edges has been used. In Example 6.2 it was only possible to match four of the friends since there were only four types of music to match them to. Thus figure 6.2 illustrates a maximal matching.

A *complete matching* is a maximal matching between two sets of equal size, so $n$ edges are used to match one set of $n$ vertices to a second set, also of $n$ vertices. Example 6.2 does not yield a complete matching since the sets are of size 5 and 4 respectively.

### THE MAXIMUM MATCHING ALGORITHM

There is a crafty algorithm to obtain a maximal matching. You begin with a matching between some of the members of the two sets in the bipartite graph. This may either be given or spotted from a table of information.

The maximum matching algorithm works by finding a tree made up of an odd number of edges that are alternately not in and then in the current matching. For example, NOT IN – IN – NOT IN – IN – NOT IN. You then exchange the IN edges for the ones that are NOT IN, in this case, three for two. Hence the number of edges in the matching goes up by one so the matching has improved. You repeat the process as necessary until the complete matching is achieved.

As with many algorithms, the overall idea is simple, but the detail is rather intricate. Example 6.3 explains the procedure in full.

### EXAMPLE 6.3

An overtime schedule is to be produced.

A can work late on Monday or Wednesday.
B can work late on Monday or Thursday.
C can work late on Tuesday, Wednesday or Friday.
D can work late on Thursday only.
E can work late on Tuesday or Friday.

One person is required to work late on each day so that all five workers work one period of overtime each.

**(a)** Initially, A offers to work on Monday. Explain why this cannot lead to a workable schedule.
**(b)** Starting with A on Monday, B on Thursday, C on Tuesday and E on Friday, use the maximum matching algorithm to obtain a complete matching.

*Solution*
**(a)** If A works on Monday, B must work on Thursday. But D can only work on Thursday. Thus there is a clash and one of B or D cannot be scheduled, so a complete matching cannot be achieved.
**(b)** The initial matching is A – Monday, B – Thursday, C – Tuesday, E – Friday. The full set of possible edges and the initial matching are shown in figures 6.3 and 6.4 respectively.

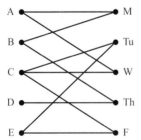

FIGURE 6.3

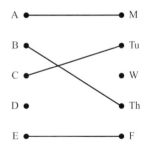

FIGURE 6.4

### Step 1
Choose a member of one set which is not in the initial matching. This would be D in this example.

**Step 2**

Having chosen D, start to form a tree of edges. At the first stage, use edges which are in the allowable graph but not in the initial matching, D – Th in this example.

FIGURE 6.5

**Step 3**

Now continue from Th, using edges which are in the allowable graph and also in the initial matching. The only possibility is Th to B.

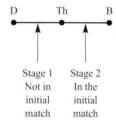

FIGURE 6.6

The algorithm continues in the same way, using another branch not in the initial matching (B – M), then another which is in the original tree (M – A). Notice that the vertices Th, B, M and A are all vertices that were present in the initial matching. Eventually you come to A – W and this introduces W into the tree – a vertex that was *not* in the initial matching. This is known as *breakthrough* and indicates that you can redraw the matching to show the improvement.

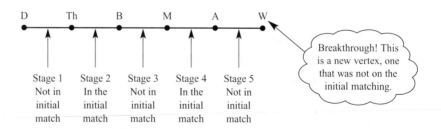

Breakthrough! This is a new vertex, one that was not on the initial matching.

FIGURE 6.7

Now look at the sequence D – Th – B – M – A – W.

From the initial matching, you remove Th – B and M – A, and replace them with D – Th, B – M and A – W. This results in the matching shown in figure 6.8.

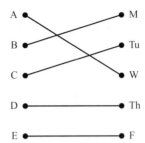

FIGURE 6.8

The number of edges in the matching has increased from four to five, the maximum possible, so you have achieved a maximal matching and the problem is fully solved.

**Note**

In this example a maximal matching was achieved after only one application of the maximum matching algorithm. Each application will match one vertex from each set so, if there is more than one unmatched vertex in each set, you will have to apply the algorithm more than once. Some questions of this type appear in the following exercise of examination-style questions.

## EXERCISE 6A EXAMINATION-STYLE QUESTIONS

1  An athletic team has six people to enter for six track events.

   A can run the 100-m and the 200-m.
   B can run the 800-m and the 1500-m.
   C can run the 200-m and the 100-m hurdles.
   D can run the 400-m, 800-m and 1500-m.
   E can run the 400-m and the 800-m.
   F can run the 100-m and the 100-m hurdles.

The captain has pencilled in **A** for the 100-m, **B** for the 800-m, **C** for the 100-m hurdles and **D** for the 400-m. Starting with this matching, apply the matching improvement algorithm to produce a complete matching.

2  A manager has five workers, Mr Ahmed, Miss Brown, Ms Clough, Mr Dingle and Mrs Evans. To finish an urgent order he needs each of them to work overtime, one on each evening, in the next week. The workers are only available on the following evenings.

   Mr Ahmed (A) – Monday and Wednesday
   Miss Brown (B) – Monday, Wednesday and Friday
   Ms Clough (C) – Monday
   Mr Dingle (D) – Tuesday, Wednesday and Thursday
   Mrs Evans (E) – Wednesday and Thursday

The manager initially suggests that A might work on Monday, B on Wednesday and D on Thursday.

(a) Draw a bipartite graph to model the availability of the five workers. Indicate, in a distinctive way, the manager's initial suggestion.

(b) Obtain an alternating path, starting at C, and use this to improve the initial matching.

(c) Find another alternating path and hence obtain a complete matching

[Edexcel]

3 Ann, Bryn, Daljit, Gareth and Nickos have all joined a new committee. Each of them is to be allocated to one of five jobs, 1, 2, 3, 4 or 5. The table shows each member's preferences for the jobs.

| Ann | 1 or 2 |
|-----|--------|
| Bryn | 3 or 1 |
| Daljit | 2 or 4 |
| Gareth | 5 or 3 |
| Nickos | 1 or 2 |

Initially Ann, Bryn, Daljit and Gareth are allocated the first job in their lists shown in the table.

(a) Draw a bipartite graph to model the preferences shown in the table and indicate, in a distinctive way, the initial allocation of jobs.

(b) Use the matching improvement alogirithm to find a complete matching, showing clearly your alternating path.

(c) Find a second alternating path from the initial allocation.

[Edexcel]

4 Five members of staff, 1, 2, 3, 4 and 5, are to be matched to five jobs, A, B, C, D and E. A bipartite graph showing the possible matchings is given on the left and an initial matching M is given on the right.

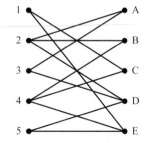 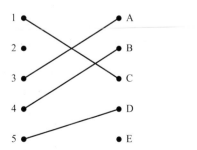

There are several distinct alternating paths that can be generated from M. Two such paths are

$$2 - B = 4 - E$$
and $\quad 2 - A = 3 - D = 5 - E.$

(a) Use each of these two alternating paths, in turn, to write down the complete matchings they generate.

Using the maximum matching algorithm and the initial matching M,

(b) find two further distinct alternating paths, making your reasoning clear.

[Edexcel]

5 At a water sports centre there are five new instructors, Ali (A), George (G), Jo (J), Lydia (L) and Nadia (N). They are to be matched to five sports, canoeing (C), scuba diving (D), surfing (F), sailing (S) and water skiing (W).

The table indicates the sports each new instructor is qualified to teach.

| Instructor | Sport |
|------------|---------|
| A | C, F, W |
| G | F |
| J | D, C, S |
| L | S, W |
| N | D, F |

Initially, A, G, J and L are each matched to the first sport in their individual list.

(a) Draw a bipartite graph to model this situation and indicate the initial matching in a distinctive way.

(b) Starting from this initial matching, use the maximum matching algorithm to find a complete matching. You must clearly list any alternating paths used.

Given that on a particular day J must be matched to D,

(c) explain why it is no longer possible to find a complete matching.

[Edexcel]

6 A rugby sevens team is to be picked from eight players. The positions in which the players can play are indicated in the table.

| | | Positions | | | | | | |
|---|---|---|---|---|---|---|---|---|
| | | 1 | 2 | 3 | 4 | 5 | 6 | 7 |
| | A | ✓ | ✓ | ✓ | | | | |
| | B | | | ✓ | ✓ | ✓ | ✓ | |
| | C | | | | ✓ | ✓ | ✓ | ✓ |
| Players | D | ✓ | | | | | | |
| | E | | | ✓ | ✓ | ✓ | | |
| | F | ✓ | ✓ | ✓ | ✓ | ✓ | | |
| | G | | ✓ | ✓ | | ✓ | | |
| | H | | | ✓ | ✓ | ✓ | ✓ | ✓ |

The coach would like to play the following players in the positions given below.

A–1; B–3; C–4; E–5; G–2; H–6

However, this would leave the team without a full-back (position 7).

(a) Find an alternating path from position 7 to an unused player. Use it to produce an improved matching corresponding to a complete team.

The game is started with the following team.

A–1; B–3; C–7; E–5; F–4; G–2; H–6

Part way through the game, H sustains an injury and D has to come on as substitute.

(b) Find an alternating path starting from D which reassigns the positions so as to allow D to come on to play in position 1.

7  At Tesafe supermarket there are five trainee staff, Homan (H), Jenna (J), Mary (M), Tim (T) and Yoshie (Y). They each must spend one week in each of five departments, Delicatessen (D), Frozen foods (F), Groceries (G), Pet foods (P) and Soft drinks (S). Next week every department requires exactly one trainee. The table below shows the departments in which the trainees have yet to spend time.

| Trainee | Departments |
| --- | --- |
| H | D, F, P |
| J | G, D, F |
| M | S, P, G |
| T | F, S, G |
| Y | D |

Initially H, J, M and T are allocated to the first department in their list.

(a) Draw a bipartite graph to model this situation and indicate the initial matching in a distinctive way.

Starting from this matching,

(b) use the maximum matching algorithm to find a complete matching. You must make clear your alternating path and your complete matching.

[Edexcel]

# KEY POINTS

1 A bipartite graph is one in which the vertices are separated into two sets. The edges are drawn to connect vertices from one set to vertices in the other.

2 In a matching each vertex is connected to at most one edge.

3 A maximal matching occurs when as many edges as possible are used in the matching. This will be the same as the number of elements in the smaller of the two separated sets.

4 If a bipartite graph comprises two sets, each of $n$ items, and a matching of $n$ edges is found, then this is a complete matching. In a complete matching, each vertex in one set is uniquely connected to one vertex in the other set.

5 The maximum matching algorithm may be used to help find a maximal matching. The procedure may be summarised as follows.

- Begin with a partial solution.
- Construct an alternating path, using first an edge that is not in the partial solution, then one that is, and so on. Continue until a vertex has been included that was not in the partial solution, so that breakthrough has been achieved.
- Amend the partial solution, by alternately adding and removing the edges used in the alternating path. This will produce an improved matching.
- Repeat the algorithm as necessary until a maximal matching has been achieved.

# Chapter seven

# FLOWS IN NETWORKS

Let me sail, let me sail, let the Orinoco flow.

*Eithne Ní Bhraonáin*

- - - - - - - - - - - - - - -

## INTRODUCING FLOWS IN NETWORKS

There are many physical situations in which something has to be transported from one place to another along alternative routes: water by pipes, electricity by cables, goods by roads, people by trains. These are modelled by networks in which the weight along each edge indicates the amount of flow along that edge.

The network should contain a single *source node*, S. At the source, all the flows are outward.

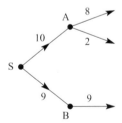

**FIGURE 7.1**

The network should also contain a single *sink node*, T. At the sink, all the flows are inward.

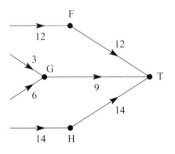

**FIGURE 7.2**

At all other nodes the *total flow in* to the node must be equal to the *total flow out* from the node. This is necessary to prevent any build-up of goods at these nodes.

Note that the edges in figures 7.1 and 7.2 are *directed*: there are arrows showing that the flow may be in one direction only. Many real networks will contain a mixture of directed and undirected edges, for example, a road system may contain both one-way and two-way roads. For the sake of simplicity, however, your A level specification will only set questions in which all of the edges are directed.

In practice, each edge has a *capacity* indicating the limit which the actual flow must not exceed. So, you label the edges with two numbers, one indicating the capacity and one the actual flow. This has the potential to be very confusing, so this book adopts the following labelling system.

- Capacities along the edges are marked as plain numbers.
- Actual flows along the edges are marked as circled numbers.

If the actual flow along an edge is equal to the capacity of that edge, then the edge is said to be *saturated*. A flow pattern in which the actual flows do not exceed the capacities and which meets the flow in = flow out condition is called a *feasible* flow pattern.

**EXAMPLE 7.1**

Figure 7.3 shows a directed capacitated network with capacities marked along the edges and actual flows marked as circled numbers.

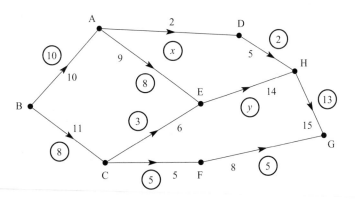

FIGURE 7.3

(a) Identify the source node and the sink node.
(b) Deduce the values of the flows *x* and *y*.
(c) Verify that the flow pattern is feasible.
(d) Name the arcs that are saturated.

*Solution*

(a) Node B has arcs leading away from it only, so B is the source node.
   Node G has arcs converging to it only, so G is the sink node.

**(b)** At A, flow in = flow out, so $10 = x + 8$, hence $x = 2$.

At E, flow in = flow out, so $8 + 3 = y$, hence $y = 11$.

**(c)** Checking each arc in turn for capacity:

BA: $10 \leqslant 10$    BC: $8 \leqslant 11$    AD: $2 \leqslant 2$    AE: $8 \leqslant 9$    CE: $3 \leqslant 6$

CF: $5 \leqslant 5$    DH: $2 \leqslant 5$    EH: $11 \leqslant 14$    FG: $5 \leqslant 8$    HG: $13 \leqslant 15$.

Checking each node in turn, except the source and the sink, for flow in = flow out:

A: $10 = 8 + 2$   C: $8 = 3 + 5$   D: $2 = 2$   E: $8 + 3 = 11$   F: $5 = 5$   H: $11 + 2 = 13$.

Thus the actual flow pattern is feasible.

**(d)** From the list of arcs above, the saturated edges are BA, AD and CF.

---

**1** The diagram below shows a feasible flow pattern for a directed, capacitated network. Actual flows are marked on the edges.

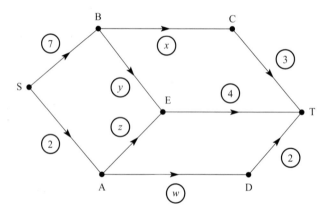

**(a)** Use the flow in = flow out principle to find the values of the flows $w$, $x$, $y$ and $z$.

**(b)** The edge SB has a capacity of 7 and all of the other edges each have a capacity of 4. State the edges that are saturated in this flow pattern.

**2** A large directed, capacitated network contains the node N, which has two edges converging on to it and two edges diverging away from it, as shown in the diagram.

The actual flows along the four edges are marked on the diagram.

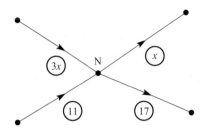

(a) Use the flow in = flow out principle to obtain an equation in $x$.

(b) Solve the equation and hence find the values of the actual flows.

**3** The diagram shows a feasible flow pattern for a directed, capacitated network. Capacities are marked along the edges and actual flows are indicated as circled numbers.

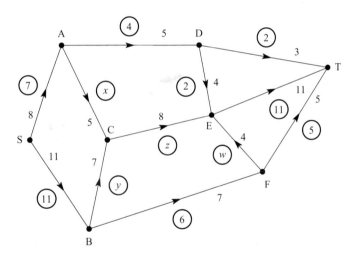

(a) State two conditions that must be met in order for this to be a feasible flow.

(b) Find the missing values of the actual flows $w$, $x$, $y$ and $z$.

The total actual flow out of the source S is 18 and the total actual flow into the sink is also 18.

(c) Explain why the total actual flow out of the source and the total actual flow into the sink must be equal.

(d) Identify the saturated edges.

(e) It is desired to raise the total actual flow from 18 to 19 by changing some of the actual flows. Suggest which ones should be changed and give their new values.

# MAXIMUM FLOW

The classic problem about flows in a network requires you to find a way of achieving a maximum flow, so that the total actual flow from source to sink is as high as possible. This means that at least some of the edges in the network must become saturated.

There are three stages to finding a maximum flow in a methodical way. The first stage is to begin with a reasonably efficient flow, which may be obtained by simple observation (*inspection*). Next, you use a technique called flow augmentation to improve the total flow until it appears that a maximum has been achieved. Finally, there is a principle called the maximum flow – minimum cut theorem that may be used to confirm that the proposed solution really is a maximum flow.

## FLOW AUGMENTATION

### EXAMPLE 7.2

Figure 7.4 shows the capacities of the edges in a directed, capacitated network.

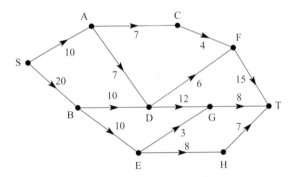

FIGURE 7.4

(a) Obtain the maximum flow along the path SBDGT and also along the path SADFT.

(b) Using SBDGT and SADFT as starting paths, apply the flow-augmentation algorithm to find an improved flow. Continue until as many edges as possible are saturated.

*Solution*

(a) The capacities of the edges making up the path SBDGT are 20, 10, 12 and 8, so the maximum possible flow along this route is 8. Similarly for SADFT the maximum flow is 6.

(b) Begin with SBDGT as a starting path. Mark the four edges with arrows pointing forwards and backwards. Mark all the backward arrows on this path with 8. This is the amount of flow on each edge and therefore indicates by how much the flow could be *reduced*, if necessary.

Mark the forward arrows to show how much unused capacity is available on each edge. For example, along SB 20 – 8 = 12. Each forward arrow indicates by how much the flow could be *increased*, if necessary.

Then mark SADFT similarly, with a back flow of 6.

Finally, on each of the unmarked edges, mark back flows of zero and forward flows equal to the capacity of the edge.

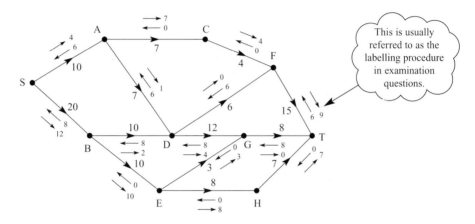

This is usually referred to as the labelling procedure in examination questions.

**FIGURE 7.5**

The next stage is to check and mark the saturated edges.

Forward arrows with a value of zero indicate saturation since the flow is at maximum capacity for that edge. At this stage the edge GT is saturated, so it is not possible to increase the flow into T along GT. Also the edge DF is saturated.

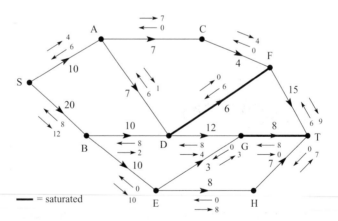

— = saturated

**FIGURE 7.6**

To augment the flow, you look for a path from S to T such that positive flow is possible along its entire length. One such path would be SACFT. The increase available using this path is 4 (being the lowest of 4, 7, 4 and 9), so you increase the flow by this amount. You increase all the backward arrows along the path SACFT by 4 and decrease all the forward arrows by the same amount, as shown in figure 7.7.

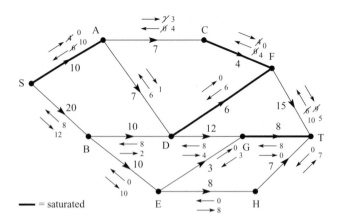

FIGURE 7.7                                    ▬▬ = saturated

The edges SA and CF are now also saturated. Further augmentation is possible, however, if you use the path SBEHT. The maximum possible increase in flow here is the minimum of 12, 10, 8 and 7, which is 7. You amend the diagram in a similar way as before.

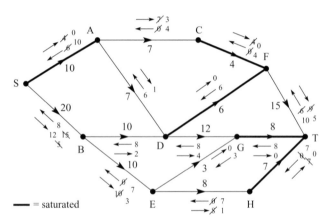

FIGURE 7.8                                    ▬▬ = saturated

Now the edge HT is also saturated. The flow appears to have been successfully maximised. The diagram is hopelessly crowded with working now so, to make the solution clear, you can redraw the diagram to show just the capacity of each edge (plain number) and the actual flow (ringed number), as shown in figure 7.9.

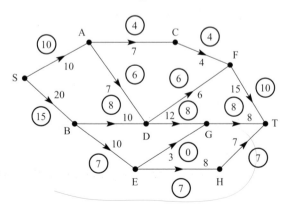

FIGURE 7.9

A brief check confirms that this solution satisfies the feasibility conditions, i.e. flow in = flow out at all nodes except S and T, and also flow ≤ capacity on each edge. Since the edges CF, DF, GT and HT are all saturated, there does not appear to be any way of increasing the flow into T at all, so the solution appears to be maximal.

The total flow out of the source is 10 + 15 = 25 and the total flow into the sink is 10 + 8 + 7 = 25, so the flow through the network is 25.

## THE MAXIMUM FLOW – MINIMUM CUT THEOREM

Suppose you split a network diagram by breaking some of the arcs in such a way that the source node falls to one side of the split and the sink node to the other side. This is called a *cut*.

The cut does not need to be a straight line but, once it crosses an edge, it must not loop back over it again. The *capacity* of a cut is simply the sum of the (positive) values of the weights along the edges that have been cut, taking their direction into account. Here are two ways of making a cut across the network in Example 7.2.

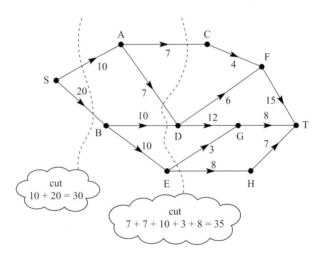

**FIGURE 7.10**

Notice that the value of the cut changes when the cut is made in different places. The value of the cut imposes an upper limit on the total possible flow through the system, and this may be succinctly stated in the maximum flow – minimum cut theorem.

> The maximum possible flow through a network is equal to the minimum value of all possible cuts.

An immediate consequence of the theorem is this: if you can find a cut equal in value to an existing flow pattern, then that flow pattern must be maximal.

Thus you can prove that the solution of a flow of 25 found in Example 7.2 is maximal if you can find a cut that takes this value. A minimum cut passes through saturated arcs or empty 'out-flowing' arcs. Such a cut is shown in figure 7.11.

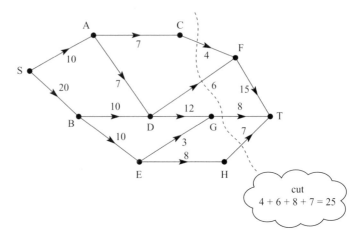

FIGURE 7.11

**Note**    It is easy to find the capacity of a cut in simple cases where the flow is generally from left to right. Watch out for situations where the flow is more confusing, as in Example 7.3 below.

**EXAMPLE 7.3**

Find the capacities of the cuts C1 and C2 shown in figure 7.12.

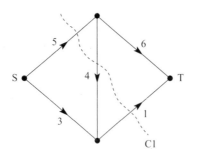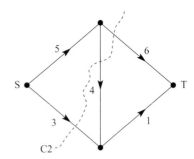

FIGURE 7.12

*Solution*    C1:  Capacity = 5 + 1 = 6    (The 4 is ignored as it does not flow from the S side of the cut to the T side.)

C2:  Capacity = 6 + 4 + 3 = 13    (All three parts count as they all flow in the right direction.)

# MULTIPLE SOURCES AND SINKS

Some problems appear to have more than one source. For example, figure 7.13 shows part of a network diagram illustrating how goods might be distributed from three depots, D1, D2, D3.

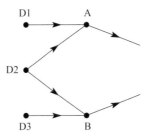

FIGURE 7.13

The methods of solution developed in this chapter depend on there being a unique source node, so it is necessary to modify the diagram. The trick is simply to create an imaginary *super-source* feeding the three source nodes.

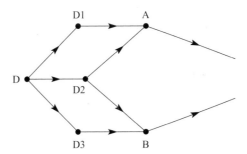

FIGURE 7.14

When capacities are marked on the diagram, the edge D to D1 is given a capacity notionally equal to the capacity from D1 to A; the capacity of D to D2 would be equal to the sum of D2 to A and D2 to B, and so on.

The same principle applies to multiple sink nodes: you simply continue them on to meet at a single *super-sink*.

EXERCISE 7B EXAMINATION-STYLE QUESTIONS

1 The diagram shows a capacitated, directed network. The number on each arc indicates the capacity of that arc.

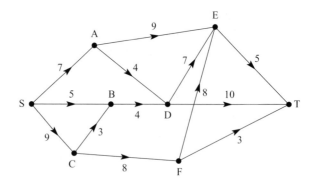

(a) State the maximum flow along
   (i) SAET
   (ii) SBDT
   (iii) SCFT.

(b) Show these maximum flows on a copy of the diagram above.

(c) Taking your answer to part (b) as the initial flow pattern, use the labelling procedure to find a maximum flow from S to T. Your working should be shown on a second copy of the diagram. List each flow-augmenting route you find, together with its flow.

(d) Indicate a maximum flow on a third copy of the diagram.

(e) Prove that your flow is maximal.

[Edexcel]

2 The diagram shows a capacitated network. The numbers on each arc indicate the capacity of that arc in appropriate units.

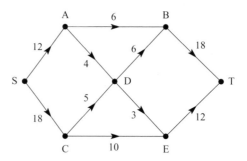

(a) Explain why it is not possible to achieve a flow of 30 through the network from S to T.

(b) State the maximum flow along
   (i) SABT
   (ii) SCET.

(c) Show these flows on a copy of the diagram.

(d) Taking your answer to part (c) as the initial flow pattern, use the labelling procedure to find a maximum flow from S to T. Show your working on a second copy of the diagram. List each flow-augmenting path you use together with its flow.

(e) Indicate a maximum flow on a third copy of the diagram.

(f) Prove that your flow is maximal.

[Edexcel]

3 A company has three warehouses, $W_1$, $W_2$, and $W_3$. It needs to transport the goods stored there to two retail outlets, $R_1$ and $R_2$. The capacities of the possible routes, in van loads per day, are shown in the diagram. Warehouses $W_1$, $W_2$ and $W_3$ have 14, 12 and 14 van loads respectively available per day and retail outlets $R_1$ and $R_2$ can accept 6 and 25 van loads respectively per day.

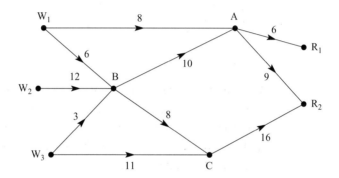

(a) On a copy of the diagram above add a super-source W, a super-sink R and the appropriate directed arcs to obtain a single-source, single-sink capacitated network. State the minimum capacity of each arc you have added.

(b) State the maximum flow along
    (i)  W $W_1$ A $R_1$ R
    (ii) W $W_3$ C $R_2$ R.

(c) Taking your answers to part (b) as the initial flow pattern, use the labelling procedure to obtain a maximum flow through the network from W to R. Show your working on a second copy of the diagram. List each flow-augmenting route you use, together with its flow.

(d) From your final flow pattern, determine the number of van loads passing through B each day.

The company has the opportunity to increase the number of van loads from one of the warehouses $W_1$, $W_2$, $W_3$, to A, B or C.

(e) Determine how the company should use this opportunity so that it achieves a maximal flow.

[Edexcel]

**4** A company wishes to transport its products from three factories, $F_1$, $F_2$ and $F_3$, to a single retail outlet R. The capacities of the possible routes, in van loads per day, are shown in the diagram.

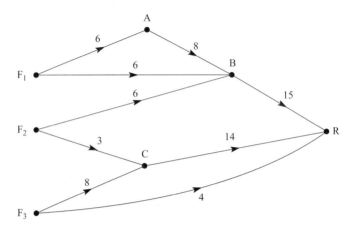

(a) On a copy of the diagram above add a super-source S to obtain a capacitated network with a single source and single sink. State the minimum capacity of each arc you have added.

(b) (i) State the maximum flow along $SF_1ABR$ and $SF_3CR$.
   (ii) Show these maximum flows on a second copy of the diagram, using number in circles.

Taking your answer to part **(b) (ii)** as the initial flow pattern,

(c) (i) use the labelling procedure to find a maximum flow from S to R. Your working should be shown on a third copy of the diagram. List each flow-augmenting route you find together with its flow.
   (ii) Prove that your final flow is maximal.

[Edexcel]

**5** The network in the diagram models a drainage system. The number on each arc indicates the capacity of that arc, in litres per second.

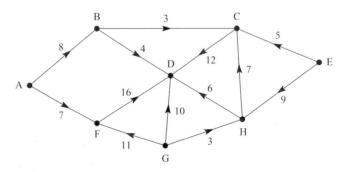

(a) Write down the source vertices.

This second diagram shows a feasible flow through the same network.

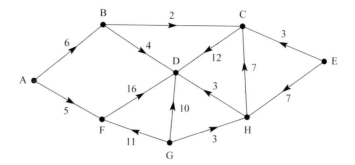

(b) State the value of the feasible flow shown in the second diagram.

Taking the flow shown in the second diagram as your initial flow pattern,

(c) use the labelling procedure on a copy of the network to find a maximum flow through it. You should list each flow-augmenting route you use, together with its flow.

(d) Show the maximal flow on a second copy of the network and state its value.

(e) Prove that your flow is maximal.

[Edexcel]

6 The diagram shows a capacitated directed network. The number on each arc is its capacity. The numbers in circles show a feasible flow from sources A and B to sinks I, J and K.

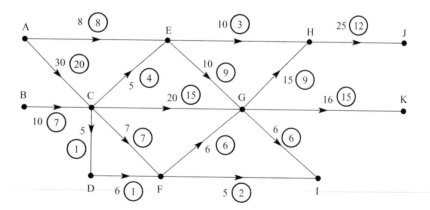

*Take this as the initial flow pattern.*

(a) On a copy of the diagram above, add a super-source S and a super-sink W to obtain a capacitated network with a single source and a single sink. State the minimum capacities of the arcs you have added.

**(b) (i)** Use the given initial flow and the labelling procedure on a second copy of the diagram to find the maximum flow through the network. You must list each flow-augmenting route you use together with its flow.

**(ii)** Verify that your flow is maximal.

**(c)** Show your maximum flow pattern on a third copy of the diagram.

[Edexcel]

**7**

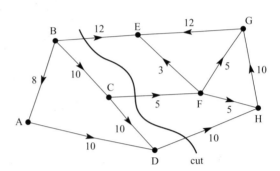

**(a)** In the transmission network shown above identify the source and the sink.

**(b)** Find the capacity of the indicated cut.

**(c)** Use flow-augmentation and the labelling procedure to find a flow pattern which gives a maximum total flow.

**(d)** Prove that your total flow in part **(c)** is maximal.

**8**

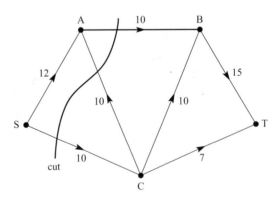

**(a)** In the transmission network shown above find the capacity of the cut.

**(b)** Use flow-augmentation and the labelling procedure to find a flow pattern which gives a maximum total flow. Prove that it is a maximum.

**(c)** Repeat parts **(a)** and **(b)** for a similar network in which the edge AC is not directed.

**9** Gas is supplied to three locations, $T_1$, $T_2$ and $T_3$, from two sources $S_1$ and $S_2$. The rate of supply from $S_1$ cannot exceed 20 units. The rate of supply from $S_2$ cannot exceed 30 units. There are no constraints on the rate of flow into $T_1$, $T_2$ and $T_3$. The transmission network is shown in the diagram, pipe capacities giving the maximum permissible rates of flow.

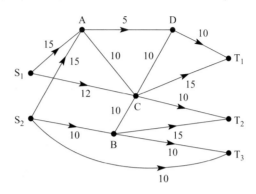

(a) Add a super-source together with appropriate capacitated edges to model the supply constraints.

(b) Add a super-sink together with appropriate edges.

(c) Find the maximum total flow through the network, saying how much is delivered to each of $T_1$, $T_2$ and $T_3$.

**10 (a)** Find minimum cuts for each of these networks.

(i)

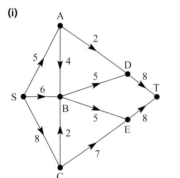

(ii)

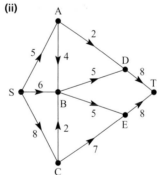

(b) Confirm that your cuts are minimum cuts by finding a flow of the same value in each network.

# KEY POINTS

1 Flows in networks are used to model movement, of goods or fluids for example, across a set of nodes, via connecting edges.

2 The network must contain a unique source node and a unique sink node. If necessary, an imaginary super-source and super-sink may be added to maintain uniqueness.

3 Edges carry weights indicating the maximum flow, or capacity, for each edge. A network diagram may also show actual flows, these are usually marked inside circles.

4 Actual flow patterns must conform to two conditions.

- The total flow in and the total flow out at each node must be equal (except for the source and sink nodes).
- The actual flow along an edge must not exceed the capacity of the edge.

An actual flow pattern that meets these conditions is known as a feasible flow.

5 The flow-augmentation algorithm begins with an initial flow pattern. Actual flows are marked with backward arrows and unused capacity with forward arrows. If a path can be identified that allows any increased flow, then the diagram is amended accordingly; this is flow augmentation.

6 Any edge for which the capacity and the actual flow are equal is called saturated. The flow-augmentation algorithm increases the number of saturated edges in the network and terminates when no further increase in flow is possible.

7 The maximum flow – minimum cut theorem states that the maximum flow across a network is equal to the minimum value of all possible cuts across its edges. This theorem is useful for verifying that a solution found by flow augmentation is indeed maximal.

# ANSWERS

## CHAPTER 1

### Exercise 1A (page 4)

1 Friday (2 + 19 + 4 = 25, becomes 82, becomes 5)

2 (a) (70, 98), (70, 28), (42, 28), (14, 28), (14, 14)
   Answer 14

   (b) (144, 360), (144, 216), (144, 72), (72, 72)
   Answer 72

3 (a) X = 26 and Y = 21

   (b) The algorithm adds $\frac{A}{B}$ and $\frac{C}{D}$, the result is $\frac{X}{Y}$.

   (c) Not exactly: the algorithm gives X = 6 and
   Y = 8, i.e. $\frac{6}{8}$ (Although this is equivalent to $\frac{3}{4}$, the
   algorithm does not contain a cancelling-down
   procedure.)

4 (a) (50, 56), (100, 28), (200, 14), (400, 7), (800, 3),
   (1600, 1) to give 2800.

   (b) The algorithm multiplies the two numbers
   together.

### Exercise 1B (page 7)

1 (a) Box 1: 2, 1, 6;    Box 2: 3, 3;
   Box 3: 5;    3 boxes are needed

   (b) Box 1: 6, 3, 1;    Box 2: 5, 3, 2

2 (a) Pipe 1: 1.2, 0.7;    Pipe 2: 1.1, 0.4, 0.4;
   Pipe 3: 0.3, 0.3, 0.2

   (b) Pipe 1: 1.2, 0.4, 0.4;    Pipe 2: 1.1, 0.7, 0.2;
   Pipe 3: 0.3, 0.3

3 (a) Plank 1: 45, 60;    Plank 2: 35, 20, 40, 25;
   Plank 3: 30, 50;    Plank 4: 55

   (b) Plank 1: 60, 55;    Plank 2: 50, 45, 25;
   Plank 3: 40, 35, 30;    Plank 4: 20

   (c) Plank 1: 60, 35, 25;    Plank 2: 55, 45, 20;
   Plank 3: 50, 40, 30

   (d) The last of these three is the most efficient, since
   it uses only three planks.

### Exercise 1C (page 11)

1 (a)
| | | | | | | | | |
|---|---|---|---|---|---|---|---|---|
| Start list | 10 | 35 | 8 | 66 | 39 | 17 | 44 | 52 |
| First pass | 10 | 8 | 35 | 39 | 17 | 44 | 52 | 66 |
| Second pass | 8 | 10 | 35 | 17 | 39 | 44 | 52 | 66 |
| Third pass | 8 | 10 | 17 | 35 | 39 | 44 | 52 | 66 |
| Fourth pass | 8 | 10 | 17 | 35 | 39 | 44 | 52 | 66 |
| Fifth pass | 8 | 10 | 17 | 35 | 39 | 44 | 52 | 66 |
| Sixth pass | 8 | 10 | 17 | 35 | 39 | 44 | 52 | 66 |
| Seventh pass | 8 | 10 | 17 | 35 | 39 | 44 | 52 | 66 |
| Eighth pass | 8 | 10 | 17 | 35 | 39 | 44 | 52 | 66 |

   (b)
| | | | | | | | | |
|---|---|---|---|---|---|---|---|---|
| Start list | 10 | 35 | 8 | 66 | (39) | 17 | 44 | 52 |
| First pass | 10 | 35 | (8) | 17 | (39) | 66 | (44) | 52 |
| Second pass | (8) | 10 | (35) | 17 | (39) | (44) | 66 | (52) |
| Third pass | (8) | 10 | 17 | (35) | (39) | (44) | (52) | 66 |
| Fourth pass | (8) | 10 | (17) | (35) | (39) | (44) | (52) | 66 |

2 Miller, Davis, Greene, Andrews, Ha, Khataria,
Costa, Smith, Oliver

3 (a)
| Initial | Pass 1 | Pass 2 | Pass 3 | Pass 4 | Pass 5 | Pass 6 | Pass 7 |
|---|---|---|---|---|---|---|---|
| 16 | 9 | 4 | 4 | 4 | 3 | 3 | 3 |
| 9 | 4 | 6 | 6 | 3 | 4 | 4 | 4 |
| 4 | 6 | 9 | 3 | 6 | 6 | 6 | 6 |
| 6 | 12 | 3 | 8 | 7 | 7 | 7 | 7 |
| 12 | 3 | 8 | 7 | 8 | 8 | 8 | 8 |
| 3 | 8 | 7 | 9 | 9 | 9 | 9 | 9 |
| 8 | 7 | 12 | 12 | 12 | 12 | 12 | 12 |
| 7 | 16 | 16 | 16 | 16 | 16 | 16 | 16 |

   (b) Bubble sort

4 (a)
| | | | | | | |
|---|---|---|---|---|---|---|
| 13 | 56 | 2 | 40 | 10 | 50 | 35 |
| 13 | 2 | 10 | 35 | (40) | 56 | 50 |
| 2 | (10) | 13 | 35 | (40) | (50) | 56 |
| 2 | (10) | 13 | (35) | (40) | (50) | 56 |

   (b)
| | | | | | | | |
|---|---|---|---|---|---|---|---|
| 7 | 6 | 5 | 4 | 3 | 2 | 1 | |
| 3 | 2 | 1 | (4) | 7 | 6 | 5 | (6 comparisons) |
| 1 | (2) | 3 | (4) | 5 | (6) | 7 | (4 comparisons) |

   In total, ten comparisons are made.

   (c) Quicksort

## Exercise 1D (page 15)

**1** JENNY, KELLY, LARA, MARTHA, NAOMI, OPAL, PANDORA

JENNY, KELLY, LARA, (MARTHA), ~~NAOMI, OPAL, PANDORA~~

~~JENNY,~~ (KELLY) LARA

(LARA)

**2** ALAN, BEN, CARLO, DEVON, EUGENE, FERGUS, GARETH, HAL, IAN

~~ALAN, BEN, CARLO, DEVON,~~ (EUGENE) FERGUS, GARETH, HAL, IAN

FERGUS, GARETH, (HAL) ~~IAN~~

FERGUS, (GARETH)

**3 (a)** Binary search.

**(b)** 16 (since $2^{16} < 100\,000 < 2^{17}$)

## Exercise 1E (page 15)

**1 (a)** 1   2   3   4   5   ⑥ ~~7   8   9   10   11~~

   ~~1   2~~ ③   4   5

        4   ⑤

**(b)** Since $2^3 < 11 < 2^4$ it is necessary to make at most three comparisons.

**2 (a)**

| | | | | | | | | | |
|---|---|---|---|---|---|---|---|---|---|
| Initial | 90 | 50 | 55 | 40 | 20 | 35 | 30 | 25 | 45 |
| Pass 1 | 50 | 55 | 40 | 20 | 35 | 30 | 25 | 45 | 90 |
| Pass 2 | 50 | 40 | 20 | 35 | 30 | 25 | 45 | 55 | 90 |
| Pass 3 | 40 | 20 | 35 | 30 | 25 | 45 | 50 | 55 | 90 |
| Pass 4 | 20 | 35 | 30 | 25 | 40 | 45 | 50 | 55 | 90 |
| Pass 5 | 20 | 30 | 25 | 35 | 40 | 45 | 50 | 55 | 90 |
| Pass 6 | 20 | 25 | 30 | 35 | 40 | 45 | 50 | 55 | 90 |

Passes 7 and 8 give the same sequence.

**(b)** Total = 475 minutes; 475 ÷ 120 = 3.958 so at least four tapes are required.

**(c)** Tape 1: 90, 30;   Tape 2: 55, 50; Tape 3: 45, 40, 35;   Tape 4: 35, 30, 25, 20; Tape 5: 20

**(d)** Tape 1: 90, 30;   Tape 2: 55, 35, 30; Tape 3: 45, 40, 35;   Tape 4: 50, 25, 20, 20

**3 (a)** Using the numbers given to represent the names:

~~1   2   3   4   5~~ ⑥ 7   8   9   10

           7   8   ⑨ ~~10~~

           7   ⑧

             ⑦

SABINE is not in the list.

**(b)** Since $2^9 < 1000 < 2^{10}$ the maximum number of iterations needed is nine.

**4**

| | | | | | | | | | |
|---|---|---|---|---|---|---|---|---|---|
| Initial | 6 | 1 | 18 | 12 | 9 | 0 | 5 | 13 | 14 |
| Pass 1 | 18 | 12 | 13 | 14 | ⑨ | 6 | 1 | 0 | 5 |
| Pass 2 | 18 | 14 | ⑬ | 12 | ⑨ | 6 | 1 | 5 | ⓪ |
| Pass 3 | 18 | ⑭ | ⑬ | 12 | ⑨ | 6 | 5 | ① | ⓪ |
| Pass 4 | 18 | ⑭ | ⑬ | 12 | ⑨ | 6 | ⑤ | ① | ⓪ |

Datchet 18;   Wraysbury 14;   Staines 13; Feltham 12;   Halliford 9;   Ashford 6;   Poyle 5; Colnbrook 1;   Laleham 0

**5 (a)**

| a | b | c | d | e | f |
|---|---|---|---|---|---|
| 645 | 255 | 2.53 | 2 | 510 | 135 |
| 255 | 135 | 1.89 | 1 | 135 | 120 |
| 135 | 120 | 1.13 | 1 | 120 | 15 |
| 120 | 15 | 8.00 | 8 | 120 | 0 |

Answer is 15

**(b)** Starting with the numbers the other way round, the first pass will flip the values of $a$ and $b$, then the second pass continues as at the start of the first solution.

**(c)** It finds the highest common factor of the numbers $a$ and $b$.

**6 (a)**

| | | | | | | | | | | |
|---|---|---|---|---|---|---|---|---|---|---|
| Initial | 55 | 80 | 25 | 84 | 25 | 34 | 17 | 75 | 3 | 5 |
| Pass 1 | 80 | 55 | 84 | 25 | 34 | 25 | 75 | 17 | 5 | 3 |
| Pass 2 | 80 | 84 | 55 | 34 | 25 | 75 | 25 | 17 | 5 | 3 |
| Pass 3 | 84 | 80 | 55 | 34 | 75 | 25 | 25 | 17 | 5 | 3 |
| Pass 4 | 84 | 80 | 55 | 75 | 34 | 25 | 25 | 17 | 5 | 3 |
| Pass 5 | 84 | 80 | 75 | 55 | 34 | 25 | 25 | 17 | 5 | 3 |

Passes 6 to 9 give the same sequence.

**(b)** Total weight ≒ 403 grams, so at least five bins are needed.

**(c)** Bin 1: 84, 5;   Bin 2: 80, 17, 3; Bin 3: 75, 25;   Bin 4: 55, 34;   Bin 5: 25

**7 (a)** Crate 1: 50, 50;   Crate 2: 50, 40; Crate 3: 40, 40, 20;   Crate 4: 30, 30, 30; Crate 5: 20
Five crates are required.

**(b)** Crate 1: 50, 50;   Crate 2: 50, 30, 20; Crate 3: 40, 40, 20;   Crate 4: 30, 30, 30
Only four crates are required.

**8 (a)**

| | | | | | |
|---|---|---|---|---|---|
| Initial | 63 | 81 | 24 | 52 | 79 |
| Pass 1 | 81 | 63 | 52 | 79 | 24 |
| Pass 2 | 81 | 63 | 79 | 52 | 24 |
| Pass 3 | 81 | 79 | 63 | 52 | 24 |
| Pass 4 | 81 | 79 | 63 | 52 | 24 |

Comparisons = 4 + 3 + 2 + 1 = 10

**(b)** They would be placed alongside each other, in the original order.

**(c)**

| | | | | | |
|---|---|---|---|---|---|
| Initial | 63 | 81 | 24 | 52 | 79 |
| Pass 1 | 63 | 81 | 52 | 79 | ⓐ24 |
| Pass 2 | 63 | 81 | 79 | ⑤52 | ㉔24 |
| Pass 3 | ㉛81 | 63 | 79 | ⑤52 | ㉔24 |
| Pass 4 | ㉛81 | ㉙79 | 63 | ⑤52 | ㉔24 |

**9 (a)** Shelf 1:  1, 1.5, 1.5, 2, 2, 2, 2.5, 3, 4;
Shelf 2:  4, 5, 5.5;   Shelf 3:  6

**(b)** Shelf 1:  6, 5.5, 5, 3;
Shelf 2:  4, 4, 2.5, 2, 2, 2, 1.5, 1.5;
Shelf 3:  1

**(c)** Shelf 1:  4, 1, 5.5, 2, 6, 1.5;
Shelf 2:  1.5, 2, 2, 4, 5, 3, 2.5

**10 (a)** $q = 13$, $r = 2$ with 13 repetitions

**(b)** Division (by repeated subtraction).

**(c)** $q_1 = 1$, $q_2 = 3$, $r = 2$.  One execution of box 4 and three of box 7.

**(d)** The second algorithm is a form of long division. More efficient, but less straightforward.

# CHAPTER 2

## Exercise 2A (page 30)

**1 (a)** 117

**(b)** DE, DB, BA, BC, CF; total length 50

**(c)** 43%

**2 (a)** Minimum connector has length 187.

**(b)** Minimum connector has length 286.

**(c)** Minimum connector has length 463.

**(d)** Minimum connector has length 523.

## Exercise 2B (page 37)

**1 (a)** Minimum connector has length 82.

**(b)** Minimum connector has length 66.

**2 (a)** AD, DE, EF, FC, CB (or AD, DE, AC, CB, CF or AD, DE, AC, CF, CB); minimum connector has length 37.

**(b)**

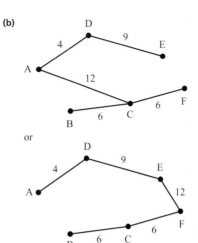

or

**(c)** No

## Exercise 2C (page 40)

**1 (a)** Minimum connector has length 38.

**(b)** Minimum connector has length 160.

**(c)** Minimum connector has length 353.

**(d)** Minimum connector has length 85.

**2 (a)** Minimum connector has length 107.

**(b)** Add HA and HB, remove AB, to obtain 106.

## Exercise 2D (page 46)

**1 (a)** SPQRT or SUVWT; 15

**(b)** SABFEDT; 8

**(c)** SBFJT; 12

**2 (a)** LA → SF → SLC → O → C; 42

**(b)** NO → C → O → D; 34

**(c)** Los Angeles to Chicago:
LA → SF → D → O → C; 42 (no quicker)
New Orleans to Denver:
NO → EP → SF → D; 31 (quicker)

**3** C: 3 + 4 + 2 + 2 + 3 = 14

**4 (a)**

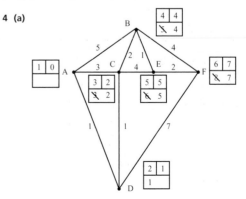

(b)  ADCBEF; length = 7

## Exercise 2E (page 50)

1  I
2  A, C, I
3  All except B
4  D
5  E, G
6  All except E
7  E, F, G, H
8  H

## Exercise 2F (page 54)

1  (a)  A Hamiltonian cycle
   (c)  Three lines all cross internally, so the graph is
        non-planar.

3  (a)  The graph would be $K_{3,3}$ which is non-planar.
   (b)  Yes, $K_{4,2}$ is planar.

4  (a)  Redraw AC above B.
   (b)  AE, CD, DE
   (c)  The graph would be $K_5$ which is non-planar.

## Exercise 2G (page 56)

1
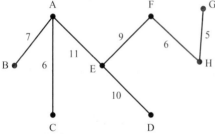
AC, AB, AE, EF, FH, HG, ED; total length 54

2  AD, DE, DC, EB; total weight 23
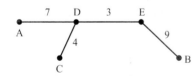

3  (a)
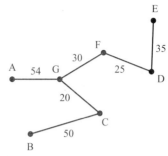
   (b)  £214 000
4  (a)  OA, AE, EC, OD, EB
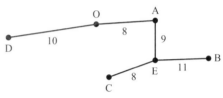
   (b)  46 m
5  (a)  Kruskal as Prim always develops connected
        partial solutions.
   (b)
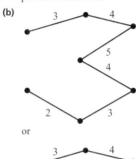
   or
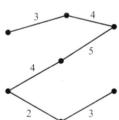
       Total weight = 21

6  (a)  ACEJ, 58 km
   (b)  Change distances to times, and add 5 to the
        weight of each edge incident upon E. New route
        ACGIJ, 62 minutes

7  (a)  SCFT, 37 km
   (b)  Using the same diagram, distance to E is 30
        using SCFE. Add ET to get SCFET with total
        weight 38 km.

8 (a) AB 6; ABC 12; ABCD 18; ABE 21; ABCF 18; ABCG 16; ABCFH 21; ABCDI 24

(b) Increases distance and changes route to G; ABCDG 23

(c) (i) Turn distances into times. Add 10 mins to each road incident upon C.

(ii) ABEF, 50 minutes

9 (a) L → Am → B → A; length = 25

(b) (i) It becomes a maximisation problem.

(ii) Update working values if greater; assign permanent label when all arcs inward have been considered.

10 (c) Three connections and three internal points, since $K_{3,3}$ is non-planar.

# CHAPTER 3

## Exercise 3A (page 66)

1 Not traversable

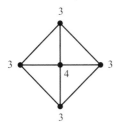

2 Not traversable

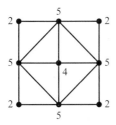

3 Fully traversable

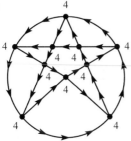

4 Not traversable

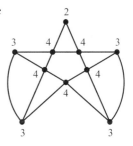

5 Fully traversable

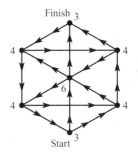

6 Semi-traversable

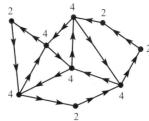

## Exercise 3B (page 70)

1 (a) Odd nodes at A, D, E, F.
Possible pairings are: AD and FE: 120 + 110 = 230;
AF and DE: 60 + 90 = 150;
AE and DF: 170 + 70 = 240
So AF and DE must be used twice.
A possible route is ABCAFGCDEDGEFA.

(b) 690 + 60 + 90 = 840 metres

2 Odd nodes at B, C, F, G.
Possible pairings are: BC and FG: 38 + 40 = 78;
BF and CG: 66 + 68 = 134;
BG and CF: 35 + 28 = 63
Total length is 440 + 35 + 28 = 503 metres
A possible route is ABGBCFCDEFGA.

**3 (a)**

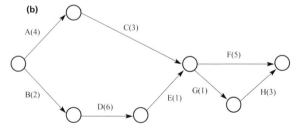

**(b) (i)** Odd nodes at A and I.
The paths covered twice are AB, BF, FE, EH and HI.

**(ii)** A possible route is ABADCEHIGFEHIFBEF BCA.

**(iii)** Total length is 91 + 22 = 113km

**4 (a)** Odd nodes at C, F, G, H.
Possible pairings are: CF and GH: 12 + 8 = 20;
CG and FH: 9 + 7 = 16; CH and FG: 9 + 10 = 19
The paths CE, EG and FH need to be traversed twice.

**(b)** By starting at C and finishing at G, the paths CE and EG no longer need to be traversed a second time, since the start and finish nodes may be of odd order.
Length = 137 + 7 = 144 metres

**5 (a)** B and E are the only odd nodes in the network.

**(b)** BE via A (BA, AE): $17 + x$;
BE via D (BD, DE): $9 + 2x$;
BE via C (BC, CE): 21

**(c)** For DE to be repeated, $x$ must satisfy two inequalities:

$9 + 2x < 17 + x \Rightarrow x < 8$

and

$9 + 2x < 21 \Rightarrow x < 6$.

Also, $x$ cannot be negative, so $0 \leqslant x < 6$.

**(d)** BE via A (BA, AE): $17 + x = 24$;
BE via D (BD, DE): $9 + 2x = 23$;
BE via C (BC, CE): 21
Total time = 12 + 12 + 14 + 9 + 11 + 10 + 21 = 89 minutes

**6 (a)** B, D, F, G

**(b)** Eulerian graphs have no odd nodes.

**(c)** BD/FG = 550, BF/DG = 250, BG/DF = 550
e.g. A → B → F → B → C → D → E → G → E → D → G → F → E → C → A, Length = 1950 + 250 = 2200

**7 (a)** A, C, F, I; need to be connected in pairs by repeated arcs to give a route which traverses all arcs.

**(b)** AC/FI = 320 m, AF/CI = 680 m, AI/CF = 680 m
2300 + 320 = 2620 m

**(c)**

| Intersection | B | C | D | E | F | G | H | I |
|---|---|---|---|---|---|---|---|---|
| Number of visits | 3 | 2 | 2 | 2 | 3 | 2 | 2 | 2 |

# CHAPTER 4

## Exercise 4A (page 81)

**1**

| Activity | Immediate predecessors |
|---|---|
| A | – |
| B | – |
| C | A |
| D | B |
| E | D |
| F | E |
| G | B, C |
| H | F, G |

**2**

| Activity | Immediate predecessors |
|---|---|
| A | – |
| B | – |
| C | – |
| D | A |
| E | B |
| F | C |
| G | D, E |
| H | F |
| I | G, H |

**3 (a)** C and E occur in the same context (i.e. in the same combinations) each time they appear in the immediate predecessors column.

**(b)**

**4 (a)** Activity E is the only activity that occurs in two different contexts, so a dummy is needed at this stage in the network.

**(b)**

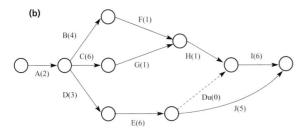

**5 (b)**

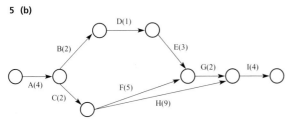

## Exercise 4B (page 89)

**1 (a)**

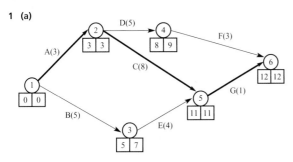

Minimum completion time 12; critical activities A, C and G

**(b)**

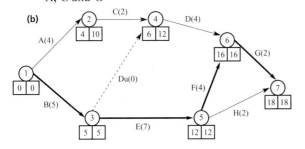

Minimum completion time 18; critical activities B, E, F and G

**(c)**

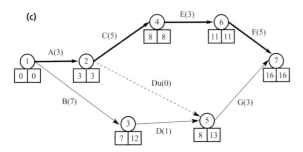

Minimum completion time 16; critical activities A, C, E and F

**(d)**

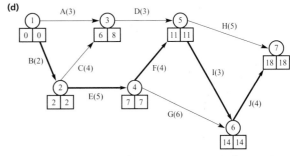

Minimum completion time 18; critical activities B, E, F, I and J

**2 (a), (b)**

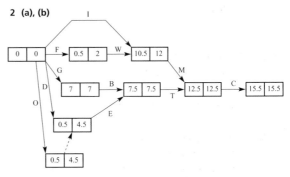

**(c)** Critical activities G, B, T and C; minimum time 15.5 minutes

**3 (a), (b)**

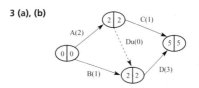

**(c)** Floats: A and D zero, B 1, C 2

**4 (a)**

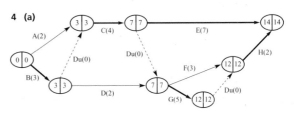

**(b)** Critical activities B, C, E, G and H

## Exercise 4C (page 95)

**1 (a), (b)**

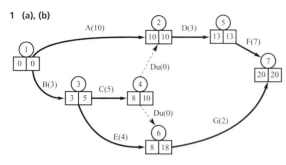

**(c)** Minimum time 20 days; critical activities A, D and F

**(d)**

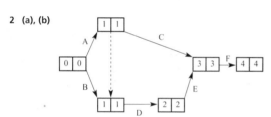

**2 (a), (b)**

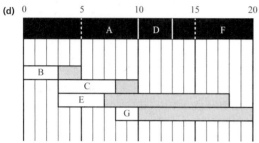

Critical activities A, D, E and F; minimum duration 4 days

**(c)** 5 days

**(d)** For example:

| Fred | A | A | C | C | D | E | E | F | |
|------|---|---|---|---|---|---|---|---|--|
| Alice | A | B | C | D | D | E | F | F | |
| | Day 1 | Day 2 | Day 3 | Day 4 | Day 5 | Day 6 | Day 7 | Day 8 | |

Can be done in 7.5 days in fact.

**3 (a)**

| Task | A | B | C | D | E | F | G | H | I |
|------|---|---|---|---|---|---|---|---|---|
| Immediate predecessor | – | – | – | – | A, B | B | B, C | D | D, E, F | F |

**(b)**

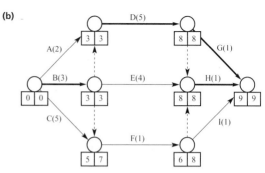

Critical activities B, D, G and H; minimum completion time 9 days

**(c)**

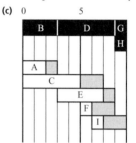

**(d)** Activities E and H need to be delayed; the shortest time is now 10 days.

## Exercise 4D (page 99)

**1 (b)**

| Activity | Duration (days) | Immediate predecessors |
|----------|-----------------|------------------------|
| A | 3 | – |
| B | 5 | A |
| C | 4 | A |
| D | 4 | A |
| E | 6 | B |
| F | 8 | C |
| G | 2 | D |
| H | 8 | E |
| I | 6 | G |
| J | 7 | E |
| K | 9 | F, H |
| L | 5 | G |
| M | 2 | I, L |

**(b)**

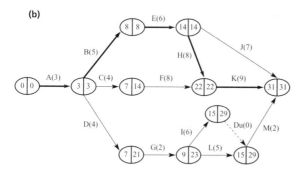

**(c)** Critical activities A, B, E, H and K; minimum time for completion 31 days

**(d)** It is needed to prevent I and L from sharing both the same start and finish nodes.

**(e)** F has a float of 7, so extending it by 8 days will increase the minimum completion time by 1 day, from 31 to 32 days.

**2 (a), (b)**

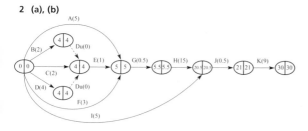

**(c)**

| Activity | | Activity start time | Activity end time |
|---|---|---|---|
| A | Cook chips | 1215 | 1220 |
| B | Toast bap | 1217 | 1219 |
| C | Prepare cheese filling | 1217 | 1219 |
| D | Cook meat | 1215 | 1219 |
| E | Make up beefburger | 1219 | 1220 |
| F | Prepare salad | 1217 | 1220 |
| G | Serve main course | 1220 | 1220.5 |
| H | Eat main course | 1220.5 | 1235.5 |
| I | Heat apple pie | 1230.5 | 1235.5 |
| J | Serve apple pie | 1235.5 | 1236 |
| K | Eat apple pie | 1236 | 1245 |

**3 (a)** Earliest time for event 6 is 15; earliest time for event 8 is 19

**(b)** Latest time for event 8 is 21; latest time for event 6 is 17

**(c) (i)** Earliest time for event 52 is 19

   **(ii)** Do not know about other activities terminating at event 58.

**(iii)** Latest time for event 50 is 17.

**(iv)** Do not know obout other activities emanating from event 35.

**4**

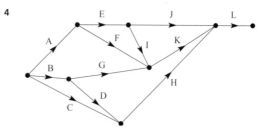

**5 (a)**

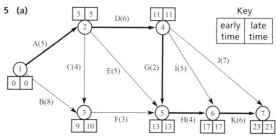

**(b)** Critical activities A, D, G, H and K; length of critical path = 23

**(c)** Three workers are required.
Worker 1: A (1–5), D (6–11), G (12–13), H (14–17), K (18–23)
Worker 2: B (1–8), E (9–13), J (17–23)
Worker 3: C (6–9), F (10–12), I (13–17)

**6 (a)** Box 1 (0, 0); Box 2 (5, 5); Box 3 (9, 10); Box 4 (12, 12); Box 5 (18, 18); Box 6 (21, 21)

**(b)** Critical activities A, C, F and H; length 21

**(c)** B 1, D 1, E 2 and G 4

**(d)**

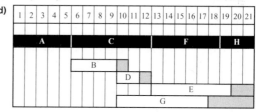

**(e)**

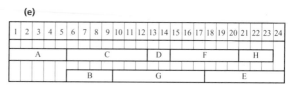

**7 (a)** Critical activities B, F, J, K and N; length 25

**(b)** A 2, C 3, D 5, E 2, G 2, H 2, I 2, L 7, M 4, P 4

**(c)**

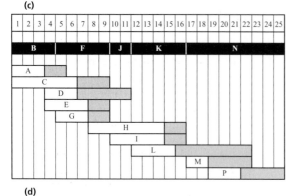

**(d)**

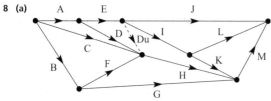

Three workers are needed.

**8 (a)**

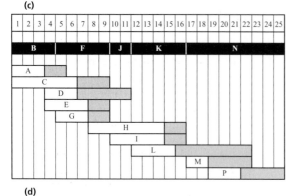

**(b)** The dummy is needed because E occurs on its own in the precedence table and also in combination with C, D and F.

**9 (a)** $x = 31$, $y = 17$

**(b)** A, C, D, E, G, J and L

**(c)** Total 107 hours; $107 \div 38 = 2.82$ so at least 3 workers will be needed.

**(d)** Worker 1: A (1–11), E (12–17), J (18–31), L (32–38)
Worker 2: B (1–8), F (12–19), I (20–30), M (31–38)
Worker 3: C (1–8), D (9–12), G (13–17), H (18–23), K (30–38)

**10 (a), (b)**

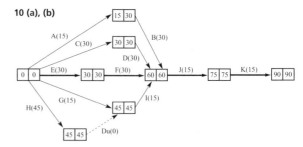

Critical activities E, F, J and K; minimum duration 90 seconds

**(c)**

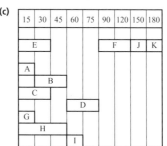

Time needed: 180 seconds

**(d)** Five

**(e)** 210 seconds, e.g.

# CHAPTER 5

## Exercise 5A (page 110)

**1**

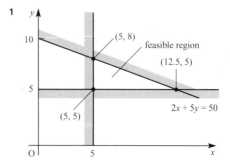

**2**

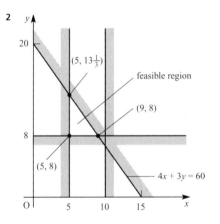

**3** $x \geqslant 2, y \geqslant 2, 25x + 40y \leqslant 500, x \geqslant 0, y \geqslant 0$

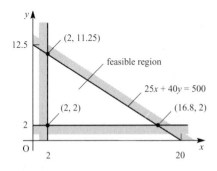

**4** $x + y \leqslant 30, x \geqslant 5, y \geqslant 5, x \geqslant 0, y \geqslant 0$

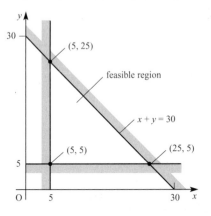

**5** $x + y \leqslant 20, 5x + 10y \leqslant 150, x \geqslant 0, y \geqslant 0$

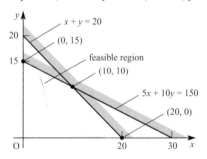

## Exercise 5B (page 113)

**1** $x = 3\frac{1}{7}; y = 2\frac{6}{7}; P = 8\frac{6}{7}$

**2** $x = 4\frac{1}{4}; y = 3\frac{1}{6}; P = 55\frac{1}{12}$

**3** Let $x$ be the number of minutes spent walking.
Let $y$ be the number of minutes spent running.
Maximise $D = 90x + 240y$
subject to $90x + 720y \leqslant 9000$
$$x + y \leqslant 30$$
Answer: $x = 20; y = 10; D = 4200$.

**4 (a), (b)** Let $a$ be the number of metres of cloth A produced.
Let $b$ be the number of metres of cloth B produced.
Maximise $P = 3a + 2.5b$
subject to $2a + b \leqslant 100$ (wool)
$$3a + 2b \leqslant 168 \text{ (dye} \times 6)$$
$$5a + 4b \leqslant 360 \text{ (loom time in minutes)}$$
$$4a + 5b \leqslant 360 \text{ (worker time in minutes)}$$
Answer: $a = 17\frac{1}{7}; b = 58\frac{2}{7}; P = 197\frac{1}{7}$ (number of £ profit)
$41\frac{1}{7}$ minutes of loom time are unused. (Sufficient to show the constraint line not intersecting the feasible region.)

**5 (a)** Let $a$ be the number of metres cut to plan A.
Let $b$ be the number of metres cut to plan B.
Maximise $I = 11a + 12b + 8(200 - a - b) = 3a + 4b + 1600$ (or maximise $3a + 4b$)
subject to $0.05a + 0.07b \leqslant 12$
$$a + b \leqslant 200$$

**(b)** Answer: $a = 100; b = 100; I = 2300$.

**6 (a)** Uses the fact that $x + y = 200$.
**(b)** $36 \leqslant 0.45x + 0.15y \leqslant 72$
**(d)** Cheapest: $x = 100; y = 100$.
Most expensive: $x = 140; y = 60$.
**(e)** $\frac{1}{10} \leqslant p \leqslant \frac{7}{10}$ giving $\frac{1}{2} \leqslant p \leqslant \frac{7}{10}$ as before.

## Exercise 5C (page 117)

**1** 13 luxury and 17 standard, giving a profit of £335 000.

**2** 14 and 2 respectively, giving a profit of £6.20.

**3** 18 small cars and 10 large cars.

**4** $x = 1; y = 2; z = 3$

**5** 66 sprockets and 21 widgets.

**6 (a)** $\frac{200}{30} = 6\frac{2}{3}$ and $\frac{200}{40} = 5$; $4x + 3y \leqslant 5100$

  **(b)** $4x + 5y \leqslant 5500$ (butter); $2x + 3y \leqslant 3000$ (sugar)

  **(c)** $I = 5x + 7y$

  **(d)** 750 biscuits and 500 buns, giving an income of £72.50.

## Exercise 5D (page 120)

**1** Let $w$ be the number of ounces of wheatgerm.
   Let $f$ be the number of ounces of oat flour.
   Minimise $C = 8w + 5f$
   subject to $2w + 3f \geqslant 7$
   $3w + 3f \geqslant 8$
   $0.5w + 0.25f \geqslant 1$
   Answer: $w = 1.25$; $f = 1.5$; $C = 17.5$.

**2 (a)** $3x + 2y$ = units of antibiotic provided.
   Must not be less than the 18 units needed.

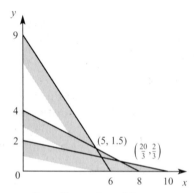

  **(b)** $x + 2y \geqslant 8$; $x + 5y \geqslant 10$

  **(c)** £3.20 at $(\frac{20}{3}, \frac{2}{3})$

  **(d)** £3.28 for 6 tablets and 1 dose

  **(e)** The integer solution, thirds of tablets being too difficult to make the saving worthwhile.
   (Or £3.26 for 7 tablets and 0.6 of a dose.)

**3** Maximum = £140; minimum = £75.

**4 (a)** Minimise $265a + 205b$
   subject to $a + b \geqslant 45$
   $13a + 10b \geqslant 500$.

  **(b)** $a = 16\frac{2}{3}$; $b = 28\frac{1}{3}$; cost = £10 225

  **(c)** $a = 10$; $b = 37$

  **(d)** Big difference in worker mix. Not much difference in cost (£10).

**5 (a)** Let $a$ hours be spent on A and $b$ hours on B.
   $a + b \leqslant 6$
   $a \geqslant 2$
   $b \geqslant 2$
   $a = 1.5b$.

  **(b)** $a \geqslant 2$ is redundant.
   Feasible points consist of the line segment joining (3, 2) to (3.6, 2.4).

  **(c) (i)** (3.6, 2.4)   **(ii)** (3, 2)

  **(d)** Putting $a = 1.5b$ in the inequalities gives $b \leqslant 2.4$, $b \geqslant \frac{4}{3}$ and $b \geqslant 2$, giving the same answer.

## Exercise 5E (page 129)

**1** $x = 3$, $y = 6$, $P = 192$ (alternatively $x = 6$, $y = 4$, $P = 192$)

**2** $x = 1$, $y = \frac{1}{3}$, $z = 0$, $P = 12\frac{1}{3}$

**3** $w = 50$, $x = 100$, $y = 0$, $z = 0$, $P = 350$

**4** $w = 66\frac{2}{3}$, $x = 66\frac{2}{3}$, $y = 0$, $z = 0$, $P = 333\frac{2}{3}$

**5** Let $m$ be the number of hours on the moped.
   Let $c$ be the number of hours in the car.
   Let $l$ be the number of hours in the lorry.

  **(a)** Maximise $20m + 40c + 30l$
   Subject to $m + c + l \leqslant 3$
   $$\frac{m}{3} + c + \frac{3l}{2} \leqslant 2.5$$
   $$20m \leqslant 55$$
   $$40c + 30l \leqslant 55$$

  **(b), (c)** Two iterations give $m = 1.625$, $c = 1.375$, $l = 0$, covering 87.5 miles.

  **(d)** Yes.
   Put the moped in the car and drive for 1.375 hours, covering 55 miles. Then use the moped for the remaining 1.625 hours covering a further 32.5 miles.

   All of the time is used and $1\frac{11}{12}$ gallons of petrol are used.

## Exercise 5F (page 131)

**1 (a)** Let $x$ be the number of club class rows and $y$ the number of economy class rows.
   The objective is to maximise income
   $(5 = 4 \times 1.25)$.
   $x + y \leqslant 30$ is the constraint on the number of rows.
   $4x + 6y \leqslant 150$ is the constraint on the number of passengers.
   $x \leqslant 10$ is the constraint on the number of club class rows.

**(b)**

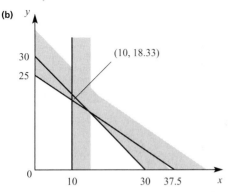

(10, 18) gives an income of 158;
(9, 19) gives an income of 159;
(8, 19) gives an income of 154;
(7, 20) gives an income of 155; etc.
Best integer solution is 9 rows of club class seats and 19 rows of economy seats.

**(c)** $x + y = 30$ and $x = 10$ intersect at (10, 20);
$4 \times 10 + 6 \times 20 = 160$

**2 (a)** Let $x$ be the number of thousands of one-litre bottles and $y$ be the number of thousands of half-litre bottles.

Maximise $\qquad 500x + 300y$
subject to $\qquad x + 0.5y \leqslant 5$
$\qquad\qquad\quad x \leqslant 4$
$\qquad\qquad\quad y \leqslant 3$

**(b)**

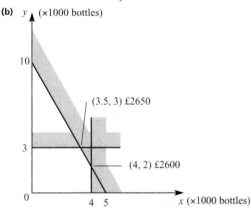

Produce 3500 one-litre bottles and 3000 half-litre bottles, giving a daily income of £2650.

**(c)** The best solution is still at the intersection of $x + 0.5y = 5$ and $y = 3$.
Thus $y = 5$ gives $x = 2.5$, producing an income of $(500 \times 2.5) + (280 \times 5) = £2650$.

**(d)** Can use 5500 litres per day, giving a daily income of £2900; £250 extra.

**3 (a)** Let $x$ kg of fruit and $y$ kg of sugar be used.
$$x \leqslant 10, \quad y \leqslant 11, \quad x \leqslant y, \quad y \leqslant \frac{4x}{3}$$

**(c)** Vertices: (0, 0), (8.25, 11), (10, 11) and (10, 10)
    **(i)** 21 kg of jam, at (10, 11)
    **(ii)** 20 kg of jam at (10, 10)
    **(iii)** 20.5 kg of jam at (9.5, 11)

**4 (a)** $x + y \geqslant 380$, $y \geqslant 125$, $2x + 4y \leqslant 1200$
**(b)** $C = 3x + 2y$
**(c)** £920, at (160, 220)
**(d)** £1300, at (350, 125)

**5 (a)** $5x + y \geqslant 10$, $2x + 2y \geqslant 12$, $\frac{1}{2}x + 2y \geqslant 6$
**(c)** $T = 2x + 3y$
**(d)** Vertices: (12, 0), $T = 24$; (4, 2), $T = 14$;
    (1, 5), $T = 17$; (0, 10), $T = 30$
    So the minimum value of $T$ is £14, when $x = 4$ and $y = 2$.

**(e)** If a third fertiliser came on the market then the problem could no longer be solved with a two-dimensional graph.

**6 (a)** $x + 2y \leqslant 70$ is the cotton fabric constraint.
    $3x + 2y \leqslant 90$ is the woollen fabric constraint.
    $x \geqslant 0$ and $y \geqslant 0$ are the non-negative constraints.

**(b)**

| Basic variable | $x$ | $y$ | $r$ | $s$ | Value |
|---|---|---|---|---|---|
| $r$ | 1 | 2 | 1 | 0 | 70 |
| $s$ | 3 | 2 | 0 | 1 | 90 |
| $P$ | −30 | −40 | 0 | 0 | 0 |

**(c)** Improvements are:

| Basic variable | $x$ | $y$ | $r$ | $s$ | Value |
|---|---|---|---|---|---|
| $y$ | 0.5 | 1 | 0.5 | 0 | 35 |
| $s$ | 2 | 0 | −1 | 1 | 20 |
| $P$ | −10 | 0 | 20 | 0 | 1400 |

and then

| Basic variable | $x$ | $y$ | $r$ | $s$ | Value |
|---|---|---|---|---|---|
| $y$ | 0 | 1 | 0.75 | −0.25 | 30 |
| $x$ | 1 | 0 | −0.5 | 0.5 | 10 |
| $P$ | 0 | 0 | 15 | 5 | 1500 |

Solution: $x = 10$, $y = 30$, $P = 1500$
**(d)** A (0, 35), C (10, 30), D (30, 0).
**(e)** Initial tableau: point O;
first improvement: point A;
second improvement: point C

**7 (a)** The basic variables $r$, $y$, $x$ appear as zeros in the $P$ row.

The other entries in the $P$ row are non-negative.

**(b)** Optimal solution: $x = 1$, $y = \frac{1}{3}$, $z = 0$, $r = \frac{2}{3}$, $s = 0$, $t = 0$, $P = 11$.

**(c)** $P = 11 - z - s - t$; the non-basic variables $(z, s, t)$ can only be changed to higher values, since they are zero already and cannot be negative.

Therefore changing any of them will decrease $P$.

**8 (a) (i)** $r$, $s$, $t$ are slack variables; they turn the inequalities into equations.

**(ii)** The final row contains the objective function $P$. Since $P = 3x + 6y + 4z$ this can be written as $P - 3x - 6y - 4z = 0$.

**(b)** First iteration:

| Basic variable | $x$ | $y$ | $z$ | $r$ | $s$ | $t$ | Value |
|---|---|---|---|---|---|---|---|
| $r$ | 1 | 0 | 1 | 1 | 0 | 0 | 4 |
| $y$ | 0.25 | 1 | 0.5 | 0 | 0.25 | 0 | 1.5 |
| $t$ | 0.75 | 0 | 1.5 | 0 | −0.25 | 1 | 10.5 |
| $P$ | −1.5 | 0 | −1 | 0 | 1.5 | 0 | 9 |

Second iteration:

| Basic variable | $x$ | $y$ | $z$ | $r$ | $s$ | $t$ | Value |
|---|---|---|---|---|---|---|---|
| $x$ | 1 | 0 | 1 | 1 | 0 | 0 | 4 |
| $y$ | 0 | 1 | 0.25 | −0.25 | 0.25 | 0 | 0.5 |
| $t$ | 0 | 0 | 0.75 | −0.75 | −0.25 | 1 | 7.5 |
| $P$ | 0 | 0 | 0.5 | 1.5 | 1.5 | 0 | 15 |

**(c)** Maximum value of $P = 15$ occurs when $x = 4$, $y = 0.5$ and $z = 0$.

**9 (a)** $3x + 2y + 4z \leqslant 35$ (processing constraint)

$x + 3y + 2z \leqslant 20$ (blending constraint)

$2x + 4y + 3z \leqslant 24$ (packing constraint)

$x \geqslant 0$, $y \geqslant 0$, $z \geqslant 0$ (non-negative constraints)

The objective function is $P = 4x + 5y + 3z$

**(b)** First iteration:

| Basic variable | $x$ | $y$ | $z$ | $r$ | $s$ | $t$ | Value |
|---|---|---|---|---|---|---|---|
| $r$ | 2 | 0 | 2.5 | 1 | 0 | −0.5 | 23 |
| $s$ | −0.5 | 0 | −0.25 | 0 | 1 | −0.75 | 2 |
| $y$ | 0.5 | 1 | 0.75 | 0 | 0 | 0.25 | 6 |
| $P$ | −1.5 | 0 | 0.75 | 0 | 0 | 1.25 | 30 |

Second iteration:

| Basic variable | $x$ | $y$ | $z$ | $r$ | $s$ | $t$ | Value |
|---|---|---|---|---|---|---|---|
| $x$ | 1 | 0 | 1.25 | 0.5 | 0 | −0.25 | 11.5 |
| $s$ | 0 | 0 | 0.375 | 0.25 | 1 | −0.875 | 7.75 |
| $y$ | 0 | 1 | 0.125 | −0.25 | 0 | 0.375 | 0.25 |
| $P$ | 0 | 0 | 2.625 | 0.75 | 0 | 0.875 | 47.25 |

Thus $P = 47.25$ is the maximum profit and this arises when $x = 11.5$, $y = 0.25$ and $z = 0$.

**(c)** The values of the slack variables are $r = 0$, $s = 7.75$, $t = 0$. Thus the company should consider increasing the time available for both processing and packing.

**10 (a)** Let $x$ tonnes of X be produced and $y$ tonnes of Y.

$200x + 100y \leqslant 1000$ (finance constraint)

$8x + 8y \leqslant 48$ (staff constraint)

$x + 3y \leqslant 15$ (space constraint)

$x \geqslant 0$, $y \geqslant 0$

**(b)** $P = 160x + 120y$

**(c), (d)** $x = 4$, $y = 2$, $P = 880$

# CHAPTER 6

## Exercise 6A (page 142)

**1** Bipartite graph

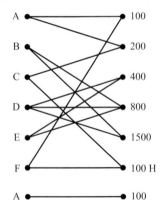

Initial allocation

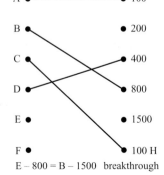

E − 800 = B − 1500   breakthrough

Improved matching

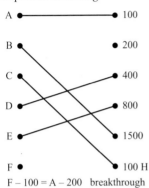

A ● ——————— ● 100

B ●              ● 200

C ●              ● 400

D ●              ● 800

E ●              ● 1500

F ●              ● 100 H

F – 100 = A – 200   breakthrough

Improved (complete) matching

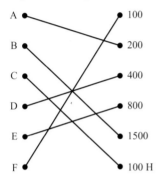

A ●              ● 100

B ●              ● 200

C ●              ● 400

D ●              ● 800

E ●              ● 1500

F ●              ● 100 H

**2 (a)** Bipartite graph and initial matching

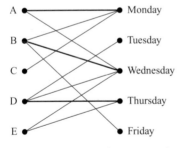

A ●              ● Monday

B ●              ● Tuesday

C ●              ● Wednesday

D ●              ● Thursday

E ●              ● Friday

**(b)** C – Mon = A – Wed = B – Fri  breakthrough

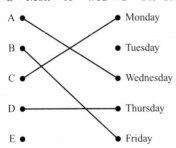

A ●              ● Monday

B ●              ● Tuesday

C ●              ● Wednesday

D ●——————— ● Thursday

E ●              ● Friday

**(c)** E – Thu = D – Tue  breakthrough

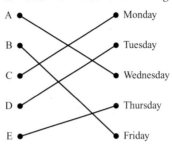

A ●              ● Monday

B ●              ● Tuesday

C ●              ● Wednesday

D ●              ● Thursday

E ●              ● Friday

**3 (a)** Bipartite graph and initial matching

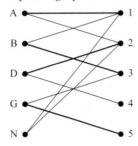

A ●              ● 1

B ●              ● 2

D ●              ● 3

G ●              ● 4

N ●              ● 5

**(b)** N – 1 = A – 2 = D – 4  breakthrough

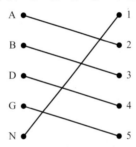

A ●              ● 1

B ●              ● 2

D ●              ● 3

G ●              ● 4

N ●              ● 5

**(c)** N – 2 = D – 4  breakthrough

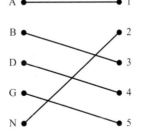

A ●——————— ● 1

B ●              ● 2

D ●              ● 3

G ●              ● 4

N ●              ● 5

(Answers **(b)** and **(c)** are interchangeable.)

**4 (a)** The path 2 – B = 4 – E leads to this complete matching.

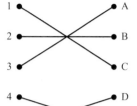

i.e. 1, 2, 3, 4, 5 match to C, B, A, E, D respectively.

The path 2 – A = 3 – D = 5 – E leads to this complete matching.

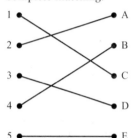

i.e. 1, 2, 3, 4, 5 match to C, A, D, B, E respectively.

**(b)** 2 – B = 4 – C = 1 – E and 2 – D = 5 – E

**5 (a)** Bipartite graph

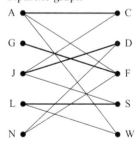

**(b)** N – D = J – S = L – W  breakthrough

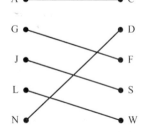

(or N – D = J – C = A – W  breakthrough, which matches A–W, G–F, J–C, L–S and N–D)

**(c)** Matching J–D means that N cannot do D, so N must do F. But G can only do F, so a complete matching is not possible.

**6 (a)** 7 – C = 4 – F  breakthrough, giving a matching as A–1, B–3, C–7, E–5, F–4, G–2, H–6

**(b)** D – 1 = A – 3 = B – 6  breakthrough, giving A–3, B–6, C–7, D–1, E–5, F–4, G–2

**7 (a)** Bipartite graph

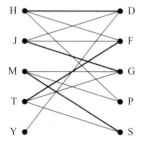

**(b)** Y – D = H – P  breakthrough

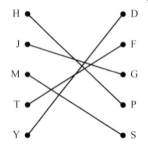

# CHAPTER 7

## Exercise 7A (page 150)

**1 (a)** $w = 2$, $x = 3$, $y = 4$, $z = 0$

**(b)** SB, BE, ET

**2 (a)** $3x + 11 = x + 17$

**(b)** $x = 3$, giving flows of 9, 11 in and 3, 17 out.

**3 (a)** At each node (except S and T), total flow in = total flow out.
Along each edge, actual flow ≤ capacity.

**(b)** $w = 1$, $x = 3$, $y = 5$, $z = 8$

**(c)** Flow cannot build up or be lost at any intermediate node, leading to the conservation principle: total flow out of S = total flow in to T.

**(d)** SB, CE, ET and FT

**(e)** Increase SA to 8, AD to 5 and DT to 3.

## Exercise 7B (page 158)

**1 (a) (i)** 5    **(ii)** 4    **(iii)** 3

**(b)**

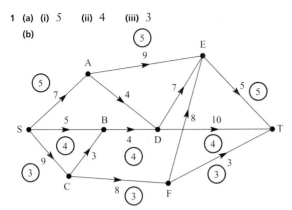

**(c)**

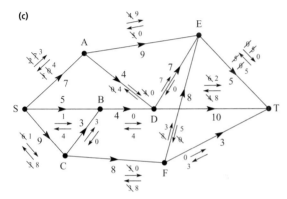

SAET −5; SCFET +5; SADT +4;
Total flow 12 + 4 = 16

**(d)**

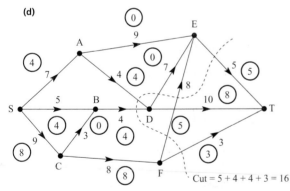

Cut = 5 + 4 + 4 + 3 = 16

**(e)** Cut of 16 (indicated above) = actual flow in **(d)**, so by the maximum flow – minimum cut theorem, this is maximal.

**2 (a)** For a flow of 30, arcs BT (18) and ET (12) would need to be saturated. But the maximum flow into B is 12, so arc BT cannot achieve an actual flow of more than this.

**(b) (i)** 6    **(ii)** 10

**(c)**

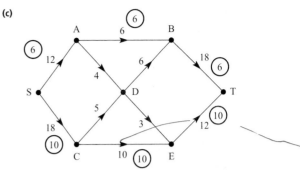

**(d)**

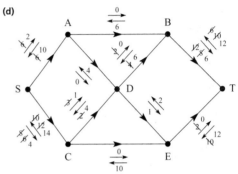

The flow augmentation paths are: SADBT adding 4, SCDET adding 2 and SCDBT adding 2, giving a maximal flow of 24.

**(e)**

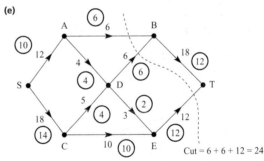

Cut = 6 + 6 + 12 = 24

**(f)** By the maximum flow – minimum cut theorem, you can prove that 24 is maximal if you can find a cut with this value. AB, DB, ET is such a cut, as marked on the diagram above.

**3 (a)**

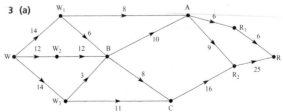

Minimum capacity for $WW_1$ = 14; $WW_2$ = 12; $WW_3$ = 14; $R_1R$ = 6; $R_2R$ = 25

**(b) (i)** 6    **(ii)** 11

(c)

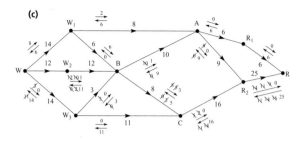

WW$_3$BCR$_2$R +3; WW$_2$BAR$_2$R +9;
WW$_1$BCR$_2$R +2; Total flow 31

(d) 14

(e) The flow is already maximal (a cut of 31 is available across arcs AR$_1$, AR$_2$, and CR$_2$).

Therefore the company does not benefit by increasing the number of van loads between the warehouses and A, B, C so no action should be taken.

4 (a) Minimum capacities: SF$_1$ 12; SF$_2$ 9; SF$_3$ 12

(b) (i) SF$_1$ABR 6; SF$_3$CR 8

(c) (i) SF$_3$R adds 4; SF$_2$CR adds 3; SF$_2$BR adds 6; SF$_1$BR adds 3.
Maximum flow is 6 + 8 + 4 + 3 + 6 + 3 = 30

(ii) A cut across arcs BR, F$_2$C, F$_3$C and F$_3$R has a capacity of 30. Hence by the maximum flow – minimum cut theorem the flow is maximal.

5 (a) A, G and E

(b) 45

(c) EHD +2; ABCHD +1; total flow 48

(d) Maximum flow = 48 using AB 7, BC 3, EC 3, EH 9, GH 3, GF 11, AF 5, BD 4, CD 12, HD 6, GD 10, FD 16

(e) Flow is maximal because all arcs leading into the sink at D are saturated. (Furthermore, there is a cut of value 48 by cutting arcs BC, BD, FD, GD, HD, CD and BC (again).)

6 (a) Connect S to A and B; SA at least 38, SB at least 10.
Connect J, K and I to W; JW at least 25, KW at least 16, IW at least 11.

(b) (i) Maximum flow = 44, developed as follows: initial flow = 35; augmentation SBCDFIW adds 3, SACGHJW adds 5, SACEHJW adds 1

(ii) Cut through arcs AE, CE, CG, FG, FI = 8 + 5 + 20 + 6 + 5 = 44

(c)

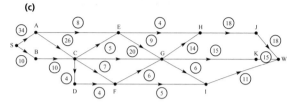

7 (a) Source = B, Sink = E

(b) 27

(c) e.g. BA = 8; BC = 7; BE = 12; AD = 8; CD = 2; CF = 5; DH = 10; FH = 0; FG = 2; FE = 3; HG = 10; GE = 12

(d) Total flow (e.g. BA + BC + BE) = 27. This is the same as the capacity of the cut in part (b), so it must be a maximal flow.

8 (a) 20

(b) e.g. SA = 10; SC = 10; AB = 10; CA = 0; CB = 5; CT = 5; BT = 15
Established flow = 20 = capacity of a cut, so flow is maximal.

(c) Cut now has capacity 30.
Can now achieve a total flow 22.
e.g. SA = 12; SC = 10; AB = 10; AC = 2; CB = 5; CT = 7; BT = 15
This can be seen to be maximal by virtue of cut S | ABCT.

9 (a) Needs SS$_1$ with capacity 20 and SS$_2$ with capacity 30.

(b) Needs T$_1$T with capacity 25 (or more), T$_2$T with capacity 25 (or more) and T$_3$T with capacity 20 (or more).

(c) Cut SS$_1$S$_2$A | BCDT$_1$T$_2$T$_3$T has capacity 47. There are many ways of achieving a flow of 47.

10 (a) (i) SABCE | DT, capacity = 15

(ii) SABC | DET, capacity = 14

(b) (i) SA = 2; SB = 6; SC = 7; AD = 2; AB = 0; BD = 5; BE = 1; CB = 0; CE = 7; DT = 7; ET = 8

(ii) As above, but with SB = 5; EB = 0; ET = 7

# INDEX